The American Singer

Second Edition

The
American Singer
Second Edition
BOOK TWO

John W. Beattie
DEAN EMERITUS, THE SCHOOL OF MUSIC, NORTHWESTERN UNIVERSITY,
EVANSTON, ILLINOIS

Josephine Wolverton
ASSISTANT SUPERVISOR, EVANSTON SCHOOLS,
ASSISTANT PROFESSOR, THE SCHOOL OF MUSIC,
NORTHWESTERN UNIVERSITY, EVANSTON, ILLINOIS

Grace V. Wilson
LATE DIRECTOR OF MUSIC, PUBLIC SCHOOLS, WICHITA, KANSAS

Howard Hinga
ASSISTANT DIRECTOR OF MUSIC, PUBLIC SCHOOLS
INSTRUCTOR OF PUBLIC SCHOOL MUSIC, EASTMAN SCHOOL OF MUSIC,
ROCHESTER, NEW YORK

American Book Company

To the Children

This music book was made for you. Some of the songs are by boys and girls of your own age. Look at the pictures, play the games, and sing and read the songs.

You will find it fun to do all these things and learn about music at the same time.

Acknowledgments

For their help in preparing this book, grateful acknowledgment is made to the following:

Elizabeth Waterman, Former Teacher of Physical Education, Chicago Public Schools, and Genevieve Reinwald, Teacher of Physical Education, Evanston Public Schools, for their contributions to the rhythm program.

Carrie Schneidewind and her second-grade class at Willard School, Evanston, Illinois, for original songs.

Elizabeth Lanigan and her class at Nathaniel Hawthorne School, Rochester, New York, for original songs.

The Bureau of American Ethnology of the Smithsonian Institution for permission to reprint "Sunrise Dance" and "Peace Pipe Song" from bulletins issued by the Bureau.

Doubleday & Company, Inc., for permission to reprint **"The Sky"** and **"The Moon"** from *Fairies and Friends* by Rose Fyleman.

Herbert Halbert for recording "All Around the Maypole" as it is sung in Mississippi.

Hall & McCreary, Publishers, for permission to reprint "My Mother" from *Melodies to Play and Sing, First Book;* and for permission to adapt the text of "A Song Story" by Mae Richardson.

Mary Allen Howarth for permission to reprint her poem "The Airplane."

Dr. Francis E. Litz for permission to reprint "Firefly" from *Poems of Father Tabb* by John Bannister Tabb.

The Macmillan Company for permission to reprint "Admonitions" from *More Silver Pennies* by Margaret Houston.

Robert McLeod of Edinburgh, Scotland, for his version of "Little Brown Bird."

Minton, Balch & Company for permission to reprint "My Whistle" from *Here and Everywhere* by Dorothy Aldis.

Dr. and Mrs. Charles Seeger for research into American folk literature.

Rebecca Tarwater of Rockwood, Tennessee, for "Skip to My Lou" as transcribed by Dr. Charles Seeger.

The University of Alabama Press for permission to reprint "Mr. Carpenter" from *Folk Songs of Alabama* by Byron Arnold.

Miguel and Cecilia Uribe of Bogotá, Colombia, for their version of the Colombian "Cradle Song."

John Work, Fisk University, Nashville, Tennessee, for "Rag Man, Bone Man."

ILLUSTRATIONS BY CORINNE MALVERN AND SCOTT MACLAIN

The American Singer

Second Edition

BOOK TWO

Sing and Dance

ROTE

Adapted

Folk Tune
used by Humperdinck

Lightly

Sing and dance and dance and sing,

All a - lone or in a ring;

Turn a - bout, in and out,

End it with a lit - tle shout. Hey!

(9)

The Sky

ROTE

Rose Fyleman   Jean Hoover

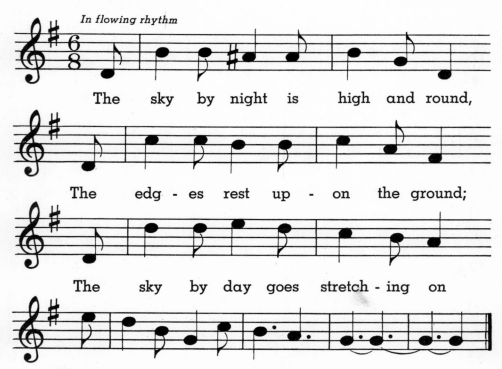

In flowing rhythm

The sky by night is high and round,

The edg - es rest up - on the ground;

The sky by day goes stretch - ing on

With - out a thing to rest up - on.____

Myself

ROTE

Julie Gibault

Earl Bigelow

Mysteriously

Who can it be there look - ing at me,

Look - ing at me from high on the shelf?

There in the mir - ror, as clear as can be,

Look - ing at me is real - ly my - self!

Mister Carpenter

ROTE

Traditional

Folk Song
sung in Alabama

Spoken: "Hello, Mister Carpenter. How can I get across
the river?"

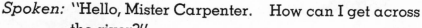

1. The bridge is down and___ can't be___ mend-ed,

Fol de rol de ri do, fol de rol de ri do;

The bridge is down and___can't be___ mend-ed,

Fol de rol de ray._____

Spoken: "But, Mister Carpenter, how deep is the river?"

2. Throw a rock, it will sink to the bottom,
   Fol de rol de ri do, etc.

Spoken: "But, Mister Carpenter, how can I get across the
river?"

3. The ducks and geese, they all swim over,
   Fol de rol de ri do, etc.

(12)

Trees in Autumn

ROTE

Norma Gillett   J. Wolverton

1. The ma-ple tree in au-tumn wears
2. The loft-y oak is dressed for fall

A gown of gay-est red;_____
In suit of red-dish brown;_____

At ev-'ry pas-ser-by who stares
He stands a-part all straight and tall

She nods her crim-son head._____
And nev-er glanc-es down._____

(13)

Go Tell Aunt Rhodey

ROTE

Early American Song

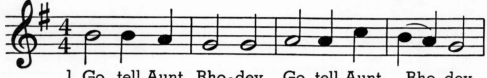

1. Go tell Aunt Rho-dey, Go tell Aunt Rho-dey,

Go tell Aunt Rho-dey The old gray goose is dead.

2. The one that she's been saving, etc.
   To make a feather bed.

3. Died last Friday, etc.,
   With aching in her head.

4. Buried last Sunday, etc.,
   Or so the preacher said.

5. Old Gander's weeping, etc.,
   Because his wife is dead.

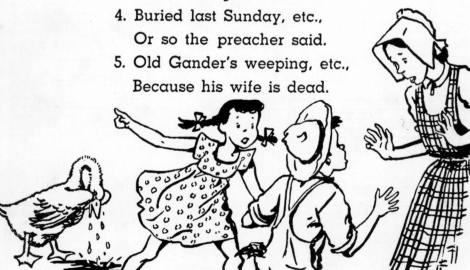

Mister Rabbit

ROTE

Traditional

Folk Song
sung in Virginia

Gaily

1. "Mis - ter Rab - bit, Mis - ter Rab - bit,
2. "Mis - ter Rab - bit, Mis - ter Rab - bit,

Your ears are might - y long!"
Your tail is might - y white!"

"Yes, my Lord, they're___ put___ on___ wrong."___
"Yes, my Lord, and I'm get - ting out of sight."___

Chorus

Ev - 'ry lit - tle soul must shine, shine, shine,___

Ev - 'ry lit - tle soul must shine,___ shine, shine.

(15)

Tommy Stout

ROTE

Based on Mother Goose   J. Wolverton

1. Oh, a - ding - a - ding - a - dong,
2. Oh, a - ding - a - ding - a - dong,

There is   some - thing ver - y   wrong,
It   will   not   be   ver - y   long

Now what is the mat-ter, pray tell?_____
Till you see the puss-y who fell;_____

Oh, my pret-ty puss-y cat
I am lit-tle Tom-my Stout,

Was a-hunt-ing for a rat,
I will pull your puss-y out,

And now she has fall-en in the well._____
From down in the bot-tom of the well._____

My Sailboat
ROTE

Mary Thom

Russel Godfrey

Slowly and smoothly

1. Go, my lit-tle boat,___ O'er wa-ters of blue,___
2. How smooth-ly you ride,___ Far out to the sea,___

So proud-ly you float,___ Sail stead-y and true.___
Now turn with the tide,___ Sail home-ward to   me.___

Autumn Wind and Rain
ROTE

Isabel Innes

Eleanor Smith

Smoothly, in moderate time

1. Hear the   drear-y   au-tumn breez-es   sigh-ing,
2. See the   yel-low   au-tumn leaves go   fly-ing,

Hear the   qui-et   pat-ter of the   rain.
See the   rain-drops   fall-ing on the   pane.

(18)

Rhythm and Melody Game

RAIN

The rain is raining all around,
It falls on field and tree,
It rains on the umbrellas here
And on the ships at sea.

Robert Louis Stevenson

1. Chant the poem.
2. Step or run lightly as you chant the poem. Turn the other way when you have chanted the word <u>tree</u>.
3. Make a melody for the poem.

The Traffic Officer

ROTE

J. W. Beattie   J. W. Beattie

1. On our way to school each day
2. Some - times when we're near - ly late

We meet a friend - ly man,
And run - ning ver - y fast,

Dressed up in a u - ni - form,
Stop - ping us, he makes us wait

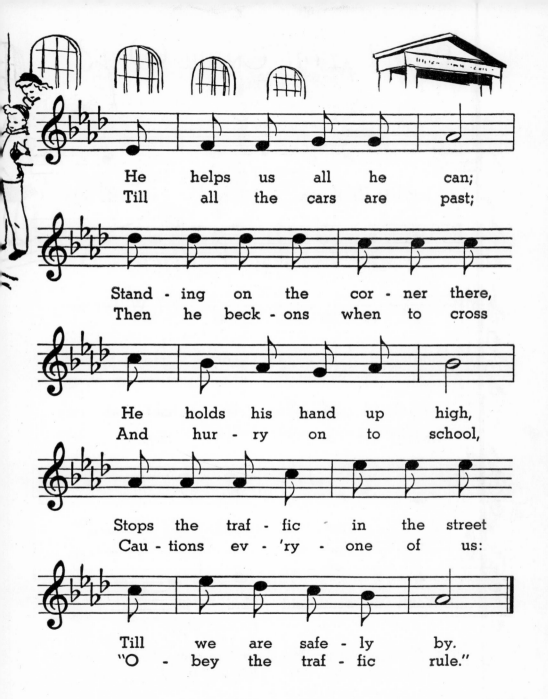

He   helps   us   all   he   can;
Till   all   the   cars   are   past;

Stand - ing   on   the   cor - ner   there,
Then   he   beck - ons   when   to   cross

He   holds   his   hand   up   high,
And   hur - ry   on   to   school,

Stops   the   traf - fic   in   the   street
Cau - tions   ev - 'ry - one   of   us:

Till   we   are   safe - ly   by.
"O - bey   the   traf - fic   rule."

Won't You Come Out?

ROTE

Adapted   French Folk Song

What shall we do to - day?_____

Won't you come out and play?_____

Shall it be tag or mar - bles,

Swing - ing or pull - a - way?_____

John is first, Bet - ty is next;

Won't you come out and play?_____

Sing about other games you could play.

This is a lively song, but there are some slow places in it. Raise your hands when you hear them.

Skip to My Lou

ROTE

Folk Song sung in Tennessee

1. Fly in the but-ter-milk, shoo, fly, shoo!

Fly in the but-ter-milk, shoo, fly, shoo!

Fly in the but-ter-milk, shoo, fly, shoo!

Skip to my lou, my dar-ling.

Chorus

Lou, lou, skip to my lou, Lou, lou, skip to my lou!

Lou, lou, skip to my lou, Skip to my lou, my dar-ling.

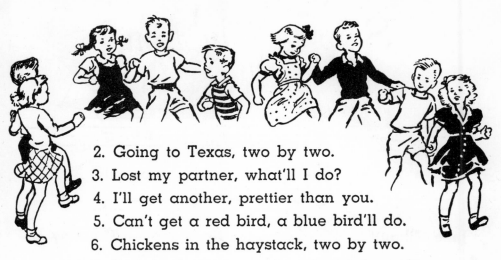

2. Going to Texas, two by two.
3. Lost my partner, what'll I do?
4. I'll get another, prettier than you.
5. Can't get a red bird, a blue bird'll do.
6. Chickens in the haystack, two by two.
7. Pig's in the fence and can't get through.
8. Hurry up, slow poke, do and do.
9. Skip a little faster, this'll never do.
10. Little red wagon, painted blue.
11. Back from Texas, how do you do?

Play this game with partners. Make a big circle. All face the center. One boy stands in the center without a partner. The boy starts singing any verse and skipping around the inside of the circle. All sing with him, and clap while he skips.

He "steals" a girl from some partner who is not watching. He skips back to place with his partner.

The entire group skips around the circle on the chorus.

The boy without a partner now starts singing and skipping, and the game is repeated.

Columbus

ROTE

Julie Gibault

Nova Scotian Chantey
(adapted)

1. Co - lum - bus sailed the o - cean blue
2. The winds blew cold, the waves rolled high,
3. And so he steered his lit - tle band

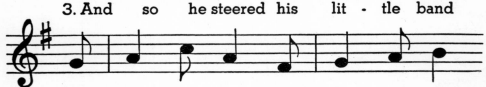

In four - teen hun - dred nine - ty - two;
No friend - ly stars were in the sky;
Un - til at last he sight - ed land;

For man - y weeks he was at sea
"Turn back!" the fright - ened sail - ors pled;
To - day we hon - or him with song:

With sail - ing ships that num - bered three.
"Sail on and on!" Co - lum - bus said.
Co - lum - bus, he - ro brave and strong.

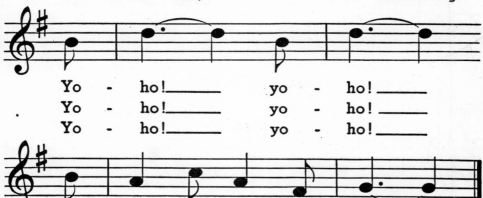

Yo - ho!_____ yo - ho!_____
Yo - ho!_____ yo - ho!_____
Yo - ho!_____ yo - ho!_____

Yo - ho, my lads, yo - ho!_____
Yo - ho, my lads, yo - ho!_____
Yo - ho, my lads, yo - ho!_____

Clouds

ROTE

J. W. Beattie

J. W. Beattie

Smoothly

1. Cloud,   cloud,   rid - ing the   sky,
2. Cloud,   cloud,   float - ing on   air,
3. Cloud,   cloud,   sail - ing a - long,

Now you   are   blue,   now   you   are   gray;
Now you   are   dark,   now   you   are   light;
Fleec - y   as   wool,   fluff - y   as   snow;

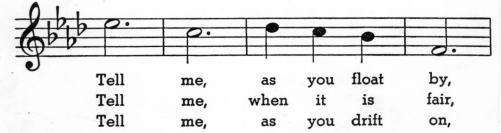

Tell   me,   as   you   float   by,
Tell   me,   when   it   is   fair,
Tell   me,   as   you   drift   on,

Will   it   be   clear   to - day?_____
Will there be   stars   to - night?_____
Will you bring   rain   to - mor - row?

The Sleeping Princess

ROTE

Adapted from a
fairy tale

Swedish Folk Tune

1. There was a pret - ty prin - cess,
2. She lived with - in a tow - er,

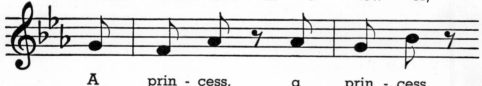

A prin - cess, a prin - cess,
A tow - er, a tow - er,

There was a pret - ty prin - cess Long a - go.
She lived with - in a tow - er Long a - go.

3. A spell was cast upon her, etc.
4. The tower was enchanted, etc.
5. The thorns grew thick around it, etc.
6. A hundred years she slept there, etc.
7. A handsome prince came riding, etc.
8. He woke the pretty princess, etc.
9. They had a royal wedding, etc.

(29)

The Mile Around

ROTE

Traditional

Game Song
played in Ohio

1. Step, step to - geth-er; Step, step to - geth-er;

Step, step to - geth-er; We'll walk a mile a - round.

2. Hop, hop a little; Hop, hop a little;
   Hop, hop a little, With one foot off the ground.

3. Jump, jump the river; Jump, jump the river;
   Jump, jump the river; For Canaan we are bound.

4. Turn, turn the corner; Turn, turn the corner;
   Turn, turn the corner; A shorter way we've found.

5. Back, back together; Back, back together;
   Back, back together; We've walked a mile around.

Make up some verses of your own for this song.

The words tell you how to play the game.

Jump Jim Crow

ROTE

American Dancing Game

Jump!   Jump!   Jump Jim Crow!

Take a lit-tle hop as a-round you go!

Jump!   Jump!   A   jump, you   know,

And take a lit-tle turn 'a-bout to jump Jim Crow.

Form a double circle, with partners facing. The words tell you how to play this game. On the third line, show your partner a new way to jump.

Blue Bird

ROTE

Traditional   American Singing Game

1. Blue__ bird,__ blue bird,   in and out the win-dow,
2. Take a lit - tle part-ner,   tap him on the shoul-der,

Blue__ bird,__ blue bird,   in and out the win - dow,
Take a lit - tle part-ner,   tap him on the shoul-der,

Blue__ bird,__ blue bird,   in and out the win - dow,
Take a lit - tle part-ner,   tap him on the shoul-der,

1, 2. O   John - ny,   I   am   tired.____

Stand in a single circle. Face the center and join hands. Lift them up to make windows. One child is the "Blue Bird" and flies in and out the windows.

On the second stanza he takes a partner. Both fly in and out the windows.

Repeat the game.

(32)

Little Brown Bird

ROTE

Paraphrased

Manx Folk Song

1. Lit - tle brown bird of the for - est deep,
2. Rocked in my nest in the ce - dar tree,

For - est deep, for - est deep,
Ce - dar tree, ce - dar tree,

When day is o - ver where do you sleep,
Safe as a babe on its moth - er's knee,

O where did you sleep__ last night?_____
O sweet was my sleep__ last night._____

Cradle Song

ROTE

Translated (adapted)   Colombian Folk Song

1. Ar - ru - ru, my ni - ño, now what shall we do?
2. Ar - ru - ru, my ni - ño, now what shall we eat?
3. Ar - ru - ru, my ni - ño, now where shall we sleep?
4. Ar - ru - ru, my ni - ño, now sleep with-out fear!

We'll wash out your dress - es and mend your old shoe.
We've on - ly a bowl full of milk warm and sweet.
To serve for a cra - dle, a box snug and deep.
No harm can be - fall you, my own ba - by dear.

¡Arruru, mi niño, qué tengo que hacer!
Lavar los pañales y hacer de comer.
¡Duérmete, mi niño, duérmete me ya!
Que viene el coquito, y te comerá.

This little lullaby is sung and loved by children who live in Colombia, South America. They sing it in Spanish. Niño is pronounced neen'yo. It means <u>child</u>, <u>baby</u>, or <u>little one</u>.

A Song Story

ROTE

Mae Richardson   Evanston children

The Basket House

Once there was a lit - tle mouse,

Look - ing for a lit - tle house,

Spied a bas - ket by the way,

Said, "I'll stay here for a day."

The Rabbit Came

Soon a rab-bit came hop-ping by,

And the bas-ket he hap-pened to spy;

"Lit - tle house, lit - tle house,

Will you be my own lit - tle house?"

"Who Are You?"

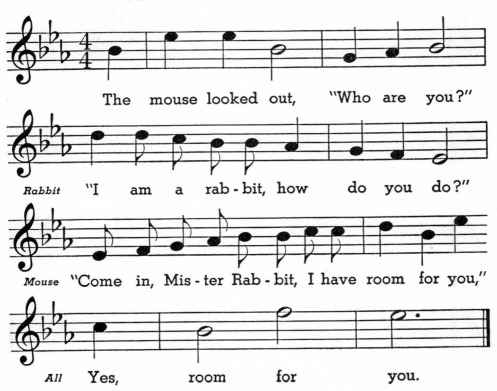

The   mouse looked out,   "Who are   you?"

Rabbit "I   am   a rab - bit, how   do you do?"

Mouse "Come in, Mis - ter Rab - bit, I have room for you,"

All Yes,   room   for   you.

The Bear Came

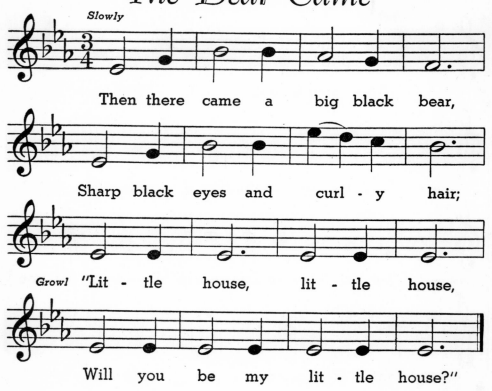

Slowly

Then there came a big black bear,

Sharp black eyes and curl - y hair;

Growl "Lit - tle house, lit - tle house,

Will you be my lit - tle house?"

"No, No, Mr. Bear"

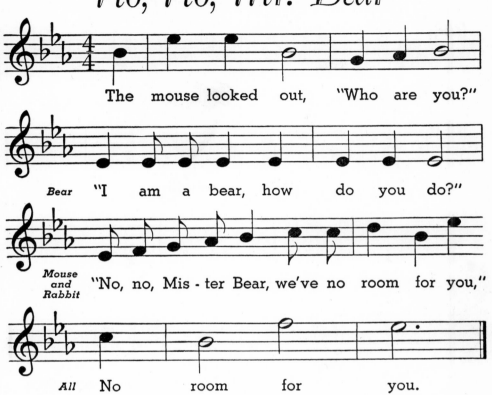

The mouse looked out, "Who are you?"

Bear "I am a bear, how do you do?"

Mouse and Rabbit "No, no, Mis - ter Bear, we've no room for you,"

All No room for you.

Crash!

The bear growled, "This is what I'll do:

I'll sit on the house and sit on you!"

(Crash!)

When you know this song story well, make a play of it and act it.

Jack-o'-Lantern

ROTE

J. W. Beattie   J. W. Beattie

1. Jack, Jack-o'-lan-tern! I won-der if you know
2. Jack, Jack-o'-lan-tern! I wish that you would tell

When you are light-ed your crook-ed teeth all show;
What you are do-ing in-side that hol-low shell;

Jack, Jack-o'-lan-tern! You are a fear-ful sight
Jack, Jack-o'-lan-tern! You're just a pump-kin head,

Out-side my win-dow this cold Oc-to-ber night.
You nev-er scare me when I am safe in bed.

(41)

My Dog

H. Hinga

ROTE

H. Hinga

1. My dog nev-er likes to stay home all the day,
2. I throw out a stick and he car-ries it back,

When school-time is o-ver he's read-y to play,
And then rac-es off on an an-i-mal track,

And wag-ging his tail and just bark-ing for fun,
So, run-ning and jump-ing and bark-ing in glee,

He leaps at my side and goes off on a run.
He chas-es the rab-bit but comes back to me.

The Melody Road

You have been singing many songs that you like.
Now try something new.
Watch the way the notes of a song go up and down.
Look at the heads of the notes, not the stems.
They look almost like a road in the country.

Going down the hill

Going up the hill

Going on a level place

Bicycle Riding

ROTE

Adapted

French Folk Tune

Well accented

1. Down the hill and up the grade,
2. Coast - ing down, but not too fast,

O - ver the ground we go roll - ing and roll - ing;
O - ver the ground we go roll - ing and roll - ing;

Through the pleas - ant sun and shade,
Now we're down, then up at last,

Roll - ing a - long on a bi - cy - cle ride.
Roll - ing a - long on a bi - cy - cle ride.

The first and third phrases look like big hills. You start at the top. You ride down and then up. See how the notes of the second and fourth phrases come down the hill. You coast down them to the bottom of the hill.

The Airplane

ROTE

Adapted

Folk Tune

1. Far   o - ver the ground, To Buf-fa - lo bound,
2. And there in the   sky, O   see it   go   by,

The air-plane is   soar-ing, The en-gines are roar-ing,
On   sil-ver wings glid-ing, A - bove the earth rid-ing,

This   time ev -'ry   day It   pass - es our   way.
So   speed - y in   flight, It's now out of   sight.

Guard at the gate: "All passengers ready to board Flight
Three at Gate Eleven."
After Stanza 1, chant what the Guard says.
Then sing Stanza 2.

Do you find any notes that go up the hill?
After you have learned to sing "Far over the ground,"
can you sing "To Buffalo bound" without any help?
What part of the third phrase can you sing?

Swinging We Go

J. W. Beattie   ROTE   Early American Waltz

Flowing

1. Float - ing down and float - ing high,
2. Smooth as silk our swing will float

Far a - bove the grass be - low,
'Neath the branch - es to and fro,

Like a swal - low in the sky,
Like a love - ly sil - ver boat,

Swing, swing - ing we go._____

Swing, swing - ing we go._____

You can make good swings to this up-and-down melody.
Make your swings very high and very low.
Bend your knees as you swing.

(47)

Falling Leaves

Isabel Innes ROTE Eleanor Vaught

1. Flut-ter-ing down, or-ange and brown,
2. Fall-ing they spread, yel-low and red,

Au-tumn leaves cov-er the coun-try and town.
Mak-ing a blan-ket for my gar-den bed.

Find the notes that go down the hill.

Rhythm and Melody Game

THE MOON

When I go walking in the dark,
The moon goes walking through the sky;
And if for fun I jump or run,
She jumps and runs the same as I.

Rose Fyleman

1. Chant the poem. It tells you some rhythms to do.
2. Make a melody for the poem.

My Fairy Friends

Harold P. Wheeler　　ROTE　　Harold P. Wheeler

Lightly

1. Fair-ies in the gar-den by the wall,
2. Gob-lins in the cel-lar eat-ing jam,

Brown-ies in the clos-ets of the hall;
Witch-es in the chim-ney eat-ing ham;

In the kit-chen cup-boards, on the shelves,
Munch-ing on the cook-ies, by them-selves,

spoken

Are the fun-ny lit-tle (sh!) elves.
Are the fun-ny lit-tle (sh!) elves.

Taking Off

ROTE

Mary L. Allen

Jean Hoover

Fast

The air - plane tax - ies up the field

And heads in - to the breeze,____

It lifts its wheels a - bove the ground,

It skims a - bove the trees,____

It ris - es high and high - er____

A - way up toward the sun,____

It's just a speck a-gainst the sky, And now it's gone.___

The melody starts low. It rises higher and higher. Then it comes down.

Good Posture

ROTE

Genevieve Reinwald

Folk Tune

There was a lit-tle boy called Slouch-y Slump,

He walked like a cam-el with a big, big hump;

No one wants to look like Slump-y, No, not at all!

You can be a big gi-raffe and stand up tall.

Sometimes Slouchy Slump sat with a big, big hump.

(51)

Lullaby

ROTE

J. W. Beattie   J. W. Beattie

1. Time   to   rest,   my   lit - tle   one,
2. Close your drow - sy   eyes   of   blue,

Shad - ows   dark   are   fall - ing;
Stars their watch are keep - ing;

Sand - man comes when day   is   done,
An - gels hov - er   o - ver   you,

At   the   door   he's   call - ing.
While you   lie   a - sleep - ing.

Fairies' Music

ROTE

Rochester children

Rochester children

Fair-ies want mu-sic when they dance on the lawn,

You know they go danc-ing from moon-rise till dawn;

So the good-na-tured trees that al-ways stand there

Just swing their long branch-es and give them an air.

Could fairies dance to this music? Could trees sway
to this music? Would you like to play fairies and trees
to this music?

(53)

The Flowers' Lullaby

ROTE

Rochester children   Rochester children

1. "Make our beds," the flow-ers said,
2. "Snow-flakes, spread your blan-ket warm,

"Make them soft and deep.
Spread it soft and white.

Rain-drops, sing your lull-a-by,
Now that we are snug in bed,

We would go to sleep."
We would say, 'Good night!'"

Find one phrase you can sing without help.

Rhythm and Melody Game

A PANCAKE

Mix a pancake,
Stir a pancake,
  Pop it in the pan;
Fry a pancake,
Toss a pancake,
  Catch it if you can.

Christina G. Rossetti

1. Make a melody for this poem. One child might sing the first two lines; another, the third. Then a third child could sing the last three lines.

2. Chant the poem. It will suggest some good rhythms for you to do. You can step, stir, toss, and hop.

Jolly Old Kangaroo

ROTE

Harold P. Wheeler   Harold P. Wheeler

Bouncily

1. A jol - ly old kan - ga - roo,
2. But man - y a trick he knew,

Who did - n't know what to do,
A lot he could tell to you,

Would hop and hop and hop and hop,
For tricks and treats and lots of eats,

He did - n't know what to do.
He thought he knew what to do.

3. Now this is the story true:
   They made him into a shoe;
   Now my feet are inside that wonderful hide
   Of that jolly old kangaroo.

(56)

Elephants

Lenore Link   ROTE   Mina Dawson

Well accented

El - e-phants walk-ing a - long the trails

Are hold - ing hands___ by hold - ing tails;

Trunks and tails are hand - y things

When el - e-phants walk___ in cir - cus rings;

And when they walk, it nev - er fails,

They're hold-ing hands by hold - ing tails.

Clickety Clackety

Julie Gibault ROTE Harold P. Wheeler

Fast and well accented

Click - e - ty clack - e - ty   click - e - ty clack - e - ty,

Hoo_____ woo! Hoo_____ woo!____   *End.*

The   train sings a click - e - ty   clack - e - ty song:

"Now   get off the track and stay where you be-long!"

It   stops at the sta - tion, then goes on its way,   *Go to the beginning.*

And   all of us hear what the   train has to say:

The Rhythm Road

Music notes show us how the melody sounds. In some songs the melody goes up, and then down. Sometimes it stays in the same place.

The notes tell us something else. They tell us that the melody is fast, like running; or that it is slow; or that it is like walking.

The notes look different, too. Some are black; some are white. Some black notes have wings on them.

walking notes   slow notes   running notes

Walking

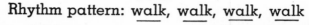

ROTE

Rhythm pattern: walk, walk, walk, walk

Evanston children   Evanston children

When we're walk - ing   down   the   street,

There   is   a   rhyme which   we   re - peat;

To   and from   our   school each   day,

You'll   hear the chil - dren's voic - es say:

Chant: Let's go walking, walking, walking,
            Let's go walking down the street;
            Let's go walking, walking, walking,
            Let's go walking, hear our feet.

Look at the lines above the notes in the first phrase.
They look almost like footsteps walking across the page.
Walk to the rhythm of this song.
Chant the rhythm as you walk.

Running

ROTE

Jean Hoover   Jean Hoover

Rhythm pattern: run, run, run, run

1. Run, run, run, run,   run, run, run, run,
2. Run, run, run, run,   run, run, run, run,

Chil - dren   all   to - geth - er;
O - ver   field   and   by - way;

Run, run, run, run,   run, run, run, run,
Run, run, run, run,   run, run, run, run,

Through the pleas - ant   weath - er.
Nev - er   on   the   high - way.

Are the sounds longer or shorter than the sounds that walk?

Running notes have wings on them to make them go faster.

On the blackboard, make the lines that run.

The Cowboy

ROTE

Mayme Christenson

Old Texan Tune

1. O - ver the prai - rie the cow-boy will ride,
2. Here he comes whirl-ing the rope in his hand,
3. Night-time is fall - ing, he o - pens his pack,

Spurs on his boots and a rope at his side;
Soon he will las - so the cat - tle to brand;
Lays out his blan - ket and sleeps on his back;

Far from the ranch house he trav - els each day,
Work now is o - ver, he gal - lops a - way,
Sad - dle for pil - low, no roof but the sky,

Yip - pee - ki! Yip - pee - ki! Yip - pee - ki - yay!
Yip - pee - ki! Yip - pee - ki! Yip - pee - ki - yay!
Yip - pee - ki! Yip - pee - ki! Yip - pee - ki - yi !

Animal Friends

ROTE

Evanston children   Evanston children

1. An - dy brought a bun - ny
2. Sal - ly brought a kit - ty
3. Bil - ly brought a dog - gie

For all of us to see;
For all of us to see;
For all of us to see;

I like the lit - tle bun - ny
I like the lit - tle kit - ty
I like the lit - tle dog - gie

And think that he likes me;
And think that she likes me;
And think that he likes me;

The bun-ny has a coat of fur
The kit-ty has some whisk-ers long
The dog-gie has a rag-ged coat

As soft as soft can be;
As fine as fine can be;
As spot-ted as can be;

I like the lit-tle bun-ny
I like the lit-tle kit-ty
I like the lit-tle dog-gie

And think that he likes me.____
And think that she likes me.____
And think that he likes me.____

What kind of notes are there in this song?
Make some more verses about animal friends.

(65)

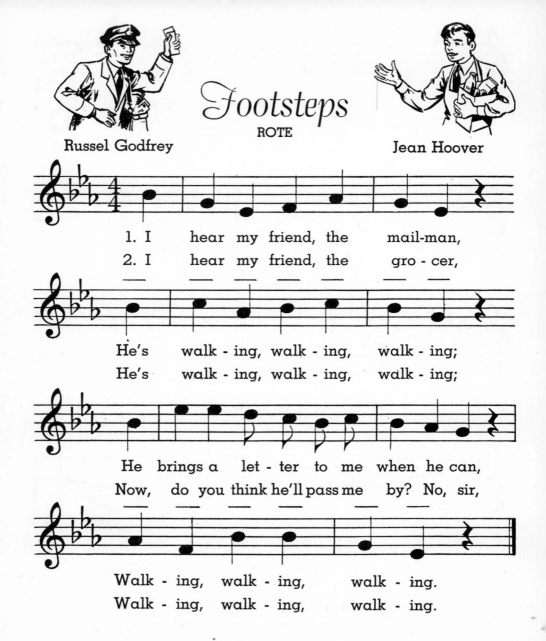

Footsteps
ROTE

Russel Godfrey

Jean Hoover

1. I hear my friend, the mail-man,
2. I hear my friend, the gro - cer,

He's walk - ing, walk - ing, walk - ing;
He's walk - ing, walk - ing, walk - ing;

He brings a let - ter to me when he can,
Now, do you think he'll pass me by? No, sir,

Walk - ing, walk - ing, walk - ing.
Walk - ing, walk - ing, walk - ing.

Make your own words about some other friends who walk by your home.

Rag Man, Bone Man

ROTE

Traditional   Old Street Cry

Rhythm pattern: <u>slow,</u>   <u>slow,</u>   <u>slow,</u>   <u>slow</u>

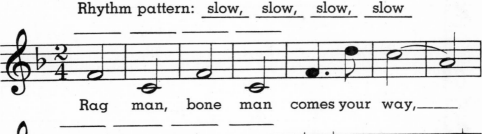

Rag   man,   bone   man   comes your way,_____

Rag   man,   bone   man,   bot-tles   to - day?_____

Well, a   big   fat   rag-pick-er   stand-ing   out   here,

Cry-ing: "Rags   and bones   and   bot-tles   to - day!"

There are many slow notes in this song.
Make some lines on the blackboard that say:
           slow   slow   slow   slow
Are they longer or shorter than walking lines?

(67)

A Boat Race

ROTE

Mary Thom

Jean Hoover

1. Pull, boys, pull, boys!
2. Pull, boys, pull, boys!

O - ver the lake we smooth - ly row.
Ev - 'ry - one keep a stead - y pace.

Pull, boys, pull, boys!
Pull, boys, pull, boys!

Fast - er a - long we go._____
Till we have won the race._____

What phrases have only slow notes in them?

Play that you are in a boat. Use two oars to row as you sing.

Now use only one paddle. Paddle on one side of the boat for a phrase, and then on the other side for a phrase.

(68)

Pattern Making

If you have drums, rattles, and sticks, you can make up some very good rhythms. Use walking, running, and slow in your patterns:

1. __ __ __ __
2. _ _ _ _ _ _ _ _
3. ____ ____ ____ ____

You can use both walking and running in one pattern. Here are some more patterns:

1. _ _ _ _ _ __ __   (run run run run walk walk)
2. __ __ ____   (walk walk slow)
3. _ _ _ _ ____   (run run run run slow)
4. __ __ _ _ _ _   (walk walk run run run run)

Play each pattern over many times.
A group of children can step your pattern as you play.

Skipping

ROTE

Audrey Carpenter

Mary Thom

Lightly and well accented

My feet go skip-ping when I'm glad,

I can-not make them walk;___

I skip a-long my way to school

And do not stop to talk;___

A hap - py feel - ing makes me skip,

My toes would like to fly,____

In work - time and play - time

I skip and don't know why.___

Skip to this song.

In the Toy Shop

ROTE — NOTE

Cecil Cowdrey   John Davey

Mid-night, mid-night, bells are sound-ing,

All the clocks are strik-ing in the town;

Out they come, the wood-en sol-diers,

March-ing through the toy shop up and down.

Find the phrases where the notes walk.

Find the running notes.   Find the slow notes.

The first and third phrases are easy to sing. Can you sing them without help? Perhaps you can sing the second phrase, too.

Thanking God

ROTE

Martha Wonn   Martha Wonn

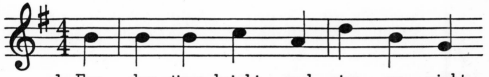

1. For day - time bright and star - ry night
2. For fam - 'ly, friends, and play - mates near

We thank Thee, heav'n - ly Fa - ther;
We thank Thee, heav'n - ly Fa - ther;

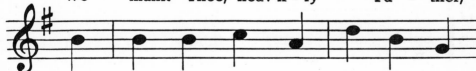

For birds and flow'rs and sun - ny hours
For school and homes and coun - try dear

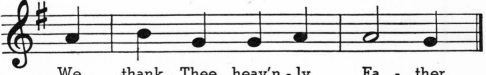

We thank Thee, heav'n - ly Fa - ther.
We thank Thee, heav'n - ly Fa - ther.

Little Johnny
ROTE

Translated   German Folk Song

1. John - ny   Rose   old - er   grows,
2. Sev - en   years,   Christ - mas nears,
3. One, two, three   peo - ple see,

Out   in - to   the   world   he   goes,
Long - ing   on   his   face   ap - pears,
Won - der   who   this   man   can   be,

Spick   and   span,   thinks   he   can
Peo - ple   know   he's   been   slow
In   the   hall   sis - ters   small

Be   a   jour - ney - man;
To   his   home   to   go;
Know   him   not   at   all;

As   he   leaves   the   old   home   place,
John - ny   now   to   John   has   grown,
Then   his   moth - er,   bent   and   gray,

Moth - er   looks   in - to   his   face,
Wants   to   be   a - mong   his   own,
Rush - es   in   the   house   to   say:

Gen - tly   sighs   fond   good - byes,
Takes   his   stick,   packs   his   grip,
"Have   no   fear!   Wel - come   here!

"Best   of   luck!"   she   cries.
Starts   the   home - ward   trip.
That's   my   John - ny   dear!"

Find the phrases where the notes go down.
Then find the phrases where the notes go up.

Santa Claus Comes

ROTE

Katherine Davis   Katherine Davis

1. I hear them, I hear them,
2. I see him, I see him,

I hear them on the roof!
I see him plain and clear!

The rein - deer are com - ing,
He's come down the chim - ney,

I hear each pranc - ing hoof!
Old San - ta Claus is here!

With a jin - gle, jin - gle bell,
In a love - ly crim - son cloak,

And   a   clop,   clop,——   clop,
With   a   sack   full   of   things,

And   a   clat - ter,   clat - ter,   clat - ter
Oh,   he's fill - ing   all   the   stock - ings

At   the   chim - ney   top;
With   the   toys   he   brings;

I   hear   them,   I   hear   them,
I   see   him,   I   see   him,

I   hear   them   on   the   roof!
Old   San - ta   Claus   is   here!

O Come, Little Children

ROTE

Translated

Thuringian Folk Song
sung in Minnesota

1. O come, lit - tle chil - dren,
2. He lies in the man - ger,
3. Now "Glo - ry to God!" comes

O come, one and all!
The hay is His bed,
The song from on high,

O come to the man - ger
The star, high in heav - en,
And "Peace for all man - kind!"

In Beth - le - hem's stall,
Shines o - ver His head,
We sing in re - ply,

And see the Lord Je - sus
And Ma - ry and Jo - seph
Then come, lit - tle chil - dren,

A - sleep in the hay,
Look down on the boy,
Be hap - py and gay,

The lit - tle Lord Je - sus
While shep - herds and wise men
For Je - sus, the Christ Child,

Was born Christ - mas Day.
Kneel down in their joy.
Was born Christ - mas Day.

O Christmas Tree

ROTE

Translated   German Folk Song

1. O   Christ-mas tree, O   Christ-mas tree,
2. O   Christ-mas tree, O   Christ-mas tree,

How   green and gay your   col - or!
I   love your glow - ing   col - or!

As   green in   win - ter's   cold and snow
Each   year when Christ - mas   time is near

As   when the sum - mer   breez - es blow;
You   bring me joy and   fun and cheer;

O   Christ-mas tree, O   Christ - mas tree,
O   Christ-mas tree, O   Christ - mas tree,

(80)   The signs ‖: :‖ mean: "Repeat."

How green and gay your col - or!

I love your glow - ing col - or!

The Simple Birth

ROTE

Paraphrased

Lowlands Christmas Song

Happily

1. A Child is born to - day, let ev-'ry-one sing!
2. A Child is born to - day, let ev-'ry bell ring!

A Child is born to - day, let ev-'ry-one sing!

A Child is born to - day, let ev-'ry bell ring!

Low - ly His birth in a rude cat - tle stall,

Free - ly He of - fers a mes-sage of cheer,

Hum-bly He came to the earth for us all.

Peace and good will and a Hap - py New Year.

(81)

Little Child of Bethlehem

Adapted   ROTE   Danish Folk Song

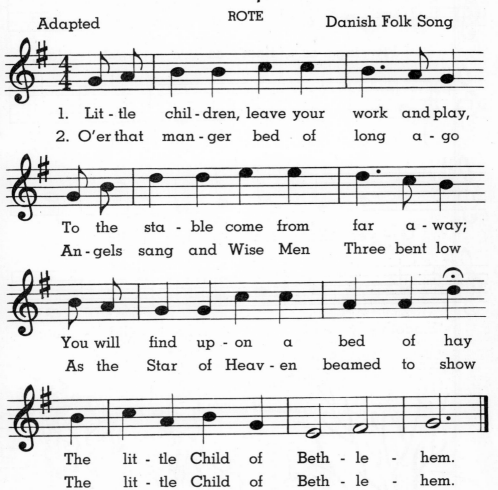

1. Lit - tle   chil - dren, leave your   work and play,
2. O'er that   man - ger   bed   of   long   a - go

To   the   sta - ble   come   from   far   a - way;
An - gels   sang   and   Wise   Men   Three   bent   low

You will   find   up - on   a   bed   of   hay
As   the   Star   of   Heav - en   beamed   to   show

The   lit - tle   Child   of   Beth - le - hem.
The   lit - tle   Child   of   Beth - le - hem.

The sign ⌢ means: "Hold the note a little longer."

Skating Song

ROTE

Norma Gillett

Lloyd Norlin

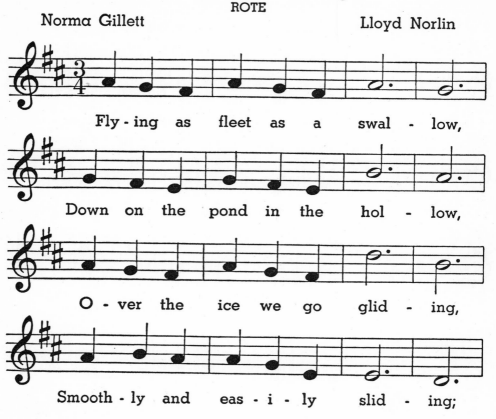

Fly - ing as fleet as a swal - low,

Down on the pond in the hol - low,

O - ver the ice we go glid - ing,

Smooth - ly and eas - i - ly slid - ing;

Hand in hand to - geth - er,

In the win - ter weath - er,

When the winds of win - ter blow,

On our skates we go._____

Skate to the music.

Coasting

ROTE

J. W. Beattie   Howard Hinga

1. It's snow - ing, it's snow - ing,
2. It's blow - ing, it's blow - ing,

What fun we'll have to - day!
Just hear the north wind bold!

Put on your coat and leg - gings
Pull tight your cap and mit - tens,

For out - door win - ter play;
The air is brisk and cold;

It's snow - ing, it's snow - ing,
It's blow - ing, it's blow - ing,

Get out your clip - per sled____
Oh, feel the i - cy blast,____

To go a - coast - ing down the hill
We'll go a - coast - ing down the hill,

And clear a path a - head.____
For win - ter's here at last.____

Steam-Up Song

ROTE

Harold P. Wheeler   Harold P. Wheeler

In fast, steady rhythm

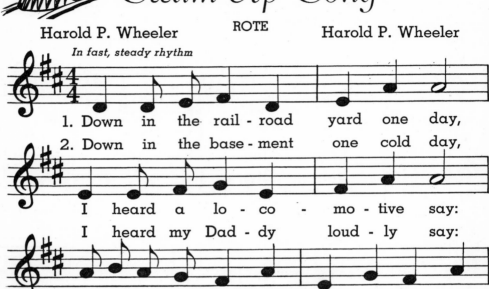

1. Down in the rail - road yard one day,
2. Down in the base - ment one cold day,

I heard a lo - co - mo - tive say:
I heard my Dad - dy loud - ly say:

"Got to get some steam up, steam up, steam up,

Got to get some steam up, steam up, steam up,

Got to get some steam up, Sss! Sss!

(88)

I just got to get some steam up!"

What phrases are alike in this song?

Admonitions
ROTE

Margaret Houston   Earl Bigelow

My Moth-er said to me: "Try to be good;

Keep your be - long - ings neat, as you should;

Say your pray'rs dai - ly be - fore you sleep;

And make no prom-ise you can - not keep."

The melody stays in the same place for a while.
Then it starts to climb. Find the highest note.

Snowflakes

ROTE

Christine Injald

Charles Crane

1. Snow - flakes are danc-ing a - bout in the air,
2. Old Moth - er Hul - da up there in the sky

Mag - ic white feath-ers come down ev-'ry-where.
Shakes out her pil-lows and feath-ers all fly.

The Swallow's Nest

ROTE

Translated

French Folk Song

Plaintively

1. Poor lit - tle one, tell me why you cry!
2. Poor lit - tle one, stop your weep-ing, do!
3. Poor lit - tle one, close your eyes and rest!

Winds rock the nest in the oak near by.
Winds of the spring-time will soon blow through.
No harm will come to the swal-low's nest.

Rhythm and Melody Game

THE SQUIRREL

Whisky, frisky, hippity hop,
Up he goes to the tree top.

Whirly, twirly, round and round,
Down he scampers to the ground.

Furly, curly, what a tail!
Tall as a feather, broad as a sail!

Where's his supper?   In the shell.
Snappy, cracky, out it fell.

1. Chant the poem.
2. Make some rhythm games to play while you chant.
3. Take turns in making a melody for the poem.

The Music Box

ROTE

Audrey Carpenter

French Folk Tune

1. Lit-tle French la-dy and lit-tle French boy
2. Lit-tle French la-dy and lit-tle French boy,

Smil-ing - ly stand on this mu - si - cal toy;
Luck - y you are to be on - ly a toy;

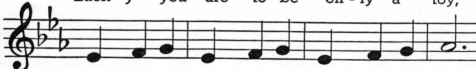

Round and a - round and a - round when it plays,
Turn - ing a - round and a - round and a - round,

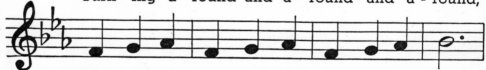

Turn-ing and turn - ing and turn - ing al - ways,
Just like a top when it spins on the ground;

They nev - er stop till the mu - sic runs down.
If you were real, you would sure - ly fall down.

(92)

What rhythm do you have in "The Music Box"?
Clap it. Step it.
Find the phrase that looks like a big slide down the hill.

Growing Up

ROTE

Evanston children   Evanston children

One lit - tle a - corn want - ed to go

Down to the ground to meet the snow;

Fa - ther Oak said: "No, no, no!

You stay here, for you must grow."

Can you make some verses of your own?

A rest 𝄽 is placed in a song instead of a walking note.

Keep your voice silent on the rest.

The Indians

The Indians lived in America a long time before the white men came.

Some Indians lived in the forest country. They built their houses of poles and strips of bark. They called their houses wigwams. They made boats of birch bark and called them canoes.

Some Indians lived on the plains, where there were few trees. They made their houses of poles and buffalo skins. They called their homes tepees.

Other Indians on the plains built their homes of grassy earth and logs. We call these houses sod houses, but the Indians called them hogans.

In the dry parts of our country, the Indians built houses of blocks of dried mud. They named these mud bricks adobe. A village of adobe houses is called a pueblo. These Indians were good farmers. They raised corn of many colors.

Indian Music

Indians have many songs and dances. They like to sing about rain and sunshine, and the sun and the moon. They have many songs about animals. They like to sing while they work. And they like to sing lullabies to the little papooses.

Indians make their instruments from many things. They make drums of wood and skins. Some Indian drums are very large. They are beaten by several men at the same time. Some Indian drums are small. Dancers hold them in their hands while they are dancing.

Indians make many kinds of rattles. They put pebbles in gourds to make loud-sounding rattles. They fasten shells and nuts on strips of leather to make rattles that are not so loud.

Grinding Corn

ROTE

Translated   Pueblo Song

Well accented

Grind - ing   corn,   grind - ing   corn,

Here   am   I,   grind - ing   corn,

Grains   of   red   and   yel - low,

Blue and white corn   I   am   grind - ing.

Form two rows.   Choose a leader in each row.
Follow her motions as she grinds the corn.

(97)

My Bark Canoe

Translated   Ojibway Song

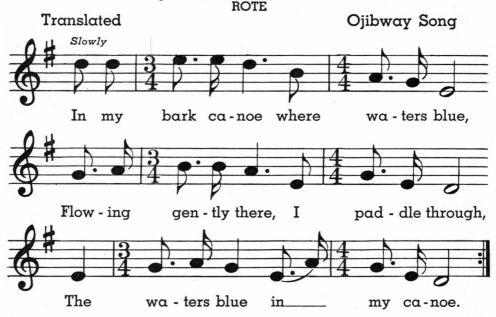

Slowly

In my   bark ca-noe   where   wa-ters blue,

Flow-ing   gen-tly there,   I   pad-dle through,

The   wa-ters blue   in____   my ca-noe.

The Indians knelt in their canoes to paddle.

Perhaps three of you can paddle in one canoe.

Watch your leader and keep with him.

Peace Pipe Song

Translated

Chippewa **Song**

Broth - ers,   sing   the   peace pipe   song,
E - hung - a,_____   e - hung - a,

As we are pass-ing the   pipe a - long;
Ga - ga-gins   o - gi   ma   e - hung - a,

Hear   my   song,   the   peace pipe   song.
E - hung - a,_____   e - hung - a.

Sit in a circle. As you sing, pass the pipe to the rhythm of the song (the first beat of each measure).

(99)

Sunrise Dance

ROTE

Teton Sioux Dance

Na na he na ha ha, Na na he na ha ha,

Na na he na ha ha, Na na he na ha ha,

Ho ho.

Make a circle. Face the drummers, who sit in the circle. While you dance around the circle, always keep facing the drummers.

1. Take a long step to the side with the right foot. This is a loud step.

2. Bring the left foot up beside the right. This is a soft step.

Repeat these two steps around the circle. The drum beats loud—soft, loud—soft all through the dance.

Indian Children

ROTE

Annette Wynne   Harold P. Wheeler

1. Where we walk to school each day,
2. And the trees were ver - y tall,
3. On - ly wig - wams on the ground,

In - di - an chil - dren used to play,
And there were no streets at all,
And at night bears prowl - ing round,

All a - bout our na - tive land,
Not a church and not a stee - ple,
What a dif - f'rent place to - day,

Where the shops and hous - es stand.
On - ly woods and In - di - an peo - ple.
Where we live and work and play.

Listening to Music

Adapted   ROTE   Beethoven

Quietly

1. When I hear love - ly mu - sic
2. All the great world of Na - ture,

As I sit at home a - lone,
Clouds and stars and grow - ing things

I can see man - y pic - tures
Move a - long with their beau - ty

Float be - fore me in the tone.
In the pic - tures mu - sic brings.

Sing a Song

ROTE

Rochester children   Rochester children

1. Sing a song ev - 'ry day,
2. Sing a song sweet and clear,

Keep your voic - es high and gay;
So that ev - 'ry - one can hear;

If ev - 'ry - bod - y sings a song,
If all of us will sing and play,

Nev - er will the world go wrong.
Hap - pi - ness will come each day.

(103)

Young Musicians

ROTE

Adapted

German Game Song

1–3. O I'm a young mu-si - cian, I like to play a tune.

Fid - dle I'm play - ing,   Hear what it's say - ing:
Trum - pet I'm play - ing,   Hear what it's say - ing:
Drum I am play - ing,   Hear what it's say - ing:

Dee - dle dum dum dum, dee - dle dum dum dum,
Toot - a - too too too, toot - a - too too too,
Rub - a - dub dub dub, rub - a - dub dub dub,

So says my fid - dle.
So says my trum - pet.
So says my drum - ming.

4. O we are young musicians, We make a jolly band;
All of us playing, Hear what we're saying:
Deedle dum dum dum, deedle dum dum dum,
Toot-a-too too too, rub-a-dub dub dub,
All making music.

Playing an Instrument

Do you have a musical instrument at home that you play? Perhaps it is made of wooden bars or metal bars. Perhaps it has strings and is played by plucking. You may have an instrument that looks like a flute.

Bring your instrument to school and learn to play some part of a song you know.

If you do not have an instrument, look around for pieces of wood or metal that can be made to give off sounds. You will be able to play a tune on them.

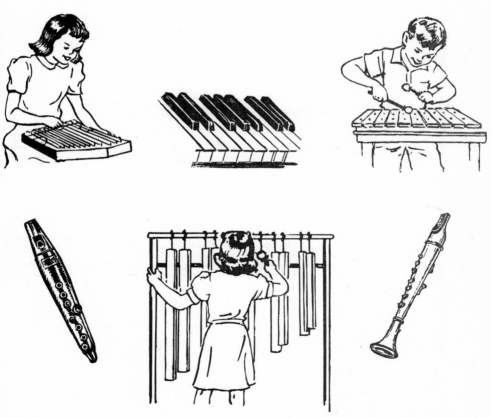

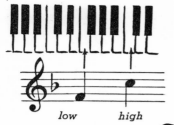

low   high

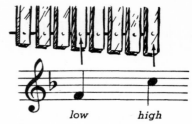

low   high

The Parade

ROTE – NOTE

Mayme Christenson   Russel Godfrey

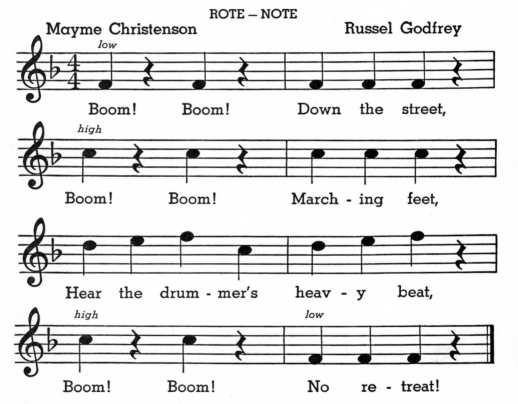

Boom!   Boom!   Down   the   street,

Boom!   Boom!   March - ing   feet,

Hear   the   drum - mer's   heav - y   beat,

Boom!   Boom!   No   re - treat!

Find the <u>low</u> note on your instruments.

Find the <u>high</u> note on your instruments.

You will now be able to play the first, second, and fourth phrases of the song.

The Streamliner
ROTE–NOTE

Mayme Christenson   Alma Spear

low   *high*

1. Hur - ry, hur - ry, see the en - gine
2. Hur - ry, hur - ry, see it speed - ing

Of   the   stream - line   train;
Like   a   sil - ver   streak;

low   *high*

Now   it's   go - ing   in   a   tun - nel,
Now   it's   com - ing, now it's go - ing,

Now   it's   out   a - gain.
Hear   the   whis - tle   shriek!

Find the slow notes.

Do the other notes walk or run?

Find the <u>low</u> notes and the <u>high</u> notes in the first and third phrases.

Play these phrases on your instruments.

Happy Builders

Jean Hoover   ROTE–NOTE   Jean Hoover

1. Saws and planes and ham - mers
2. Work - ing all to - geth - er,

Are more fun than toys;
Hap - py girls and boys;

1, 2. Bing! Bang! Bing! Bang!

Such a jol - ly noise!

Find the low notes and the high notes in the third phrase. Find the new note for low. It is different from the low note in "The Parade."

Play the third phrase on your instruments.

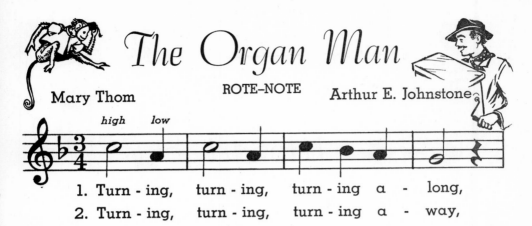

The Organ Man

ROTE–NOTE

Mary Thom   Arthur E. Johnstone

high   low

1. Turn - ing,   turn - ing,   turn - ing a - long,
2. Turn - ing,   turn - ing,   turn - ing a - way,

Hear   the   or - gan man   play   a   song.
So   the   chil-dren may   dance and   play.

You will be able to play the first four notes.
Sing the rest of the song with words.

Rhythm Game

In this game, one child beats a rhythm pattern. A second child answers it just as it was played. You may use rhythm sticks, drums, or clapping.

Here are fast and slow patterns:

1. _ _ _ _ _ ___   run run run run slow
2. ___ ___ ___ _ _ _ _   slow slow run run run run

Here are loud and soft patterns:

1. > > > _ _ _   loud loud loud soft soft soft
2. > _ _ > _ _   loud soft soft loud soft soft

(109)

Mozart
ROTE

Adapted   Mozart

In moderate time

1. Long a - go in old Vi - en - na
2. Though we may not make our mu - sic

A young boy mu - si - cian,
As well as did Mo - zart,

Lit - tle Mo - zart, dressed in vel - vet,
Ev - 'ry time we sing to - geth - er

Per - formed for the king.
What pleas - ure we bring!

Mozart played music and made melodies when he was a little boy. He became a famous composer.

Boys
ROTE–NOTE

Isabel Innes

Eleanor Smith

1. Jack - y was a far - mer boy
2. Jim - my was a vil - lage boy
3. Bob - by was a cit - y boy,

Who plant - ed grass and clo - ver,
Who wan - dered to the wood - lot,
He nev - er had gone fish - ing,

Cut it on a sum - mer day
Tried to ride a bil - ly goat,
Found he could not bait a hook

And then he raked it o - ver.
His fa - ther said he could not.
By sit - ting down and wish - ing.

Can you sing and play the first phrase?
Is the third phrase the same as the first phrase?

February Birthdays

ROTE

Adapted

Old Tune
sung in Illinois

Brightly

1. Two fa-mous men were born in Feb-ru - ar - y,____
2. The twelfth of Feb-ru - ar-y is for Lin-coln,____
3. George Wash-ing-ton was born the twen-ty - sec-ond,____

Two fa - mous men were born in Feb - ru - ar - y,____

The twelfth of Feb-ru - ar - y is for Lin-coln,___

George Wash-ing-ton was born the twen-ty - sec-ond,___

Two fa - mous men were born in Feb - ru - ar - y,____

The twelfth of Feb-ru - ar - y is for Lin-coln,___

George Wash-ing-ton was born the twen-ty - sec-ond,___

Hur - rah for Pres - i - dents ____ great!____
Hur - rah for Lin-coln's birth - day!____
Hur - rah for Wash-ing - ton's birth - day!____

(112)

Our Flag

ROTE

Mary Thom   Eleanor Smith

1. On high a - bove the school-house,
2. We prom - ise to be loy - al,

And in our class - room, too,
With mind and spir - it true,

We see our star - ry ban - ner,
As we sa - lute our ban - ner,

Our own red, white, and blue.
Our own red, white, and blue.

THE PLEDGE OF ALLEGIANCE

I pledge allegiance to the flag of the United States of America and to the Republic for which it stands: one nation, indivisible, with liberty and justice for all.

A Valentine

ROTE

Virginia Murdock   Ann Donaldson

Here is a heart, some lace, and glue,

Here are the let - ters, "I love you."

Can you guess what we will do?

Make it and give it to Moth - er.

My Valentine

ROTE

Evanston children Evanston children

In moderate time

O Val - en - tine, O Val - en - tine,

Will you be my Val - en - tine?

If you like me as I like you,

You'll nod your head and say: "I do."

The sun and all the stars will shine

If you will be my Val - en - tine.

The Carrier Pigeon

ROTE

Translated

German Folk Song
sung in Wisconsin

1. Once a pi - geon came fly - ing,
2. And I sent back a mes - sage,

And he sat at my feet,
My own true love to greet,

For he brought me a mes - sage
By the car - ri - er pi - geon

From my true love so sweet.
That had sat at my feet.

The Reading Road

You have seen the <u>high</u> notes and the <u>low</u> notes of a song.

You have seen that some of the notes have walking rhythm. Some have running rhythm. Some have slow rhythm.

Now, here is a tonal pattern:

Sing the tonal pattern with some new names, called syllables.

Building Game

Cut five notes out of black paper. Make them the size of a twenty-five-cent piece. Put the notes in an envelope, so that you will have them when you play this game.

Now sing the tonal pattern. Then put the two notes where they belong on the staff in the back of your book. Build all the tonal patterns you know.

The Cuckoo Clock

ROTE — NOTE

Norma Gillett

J. W. Beattie

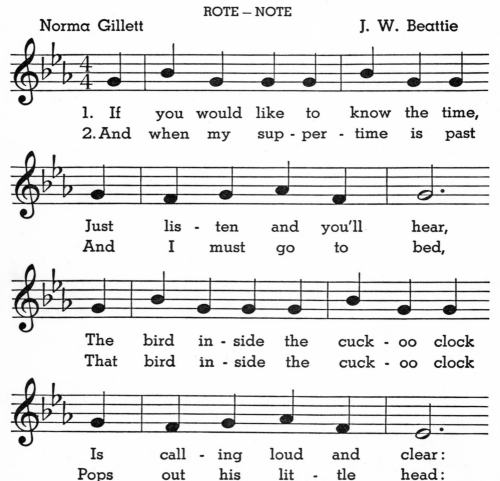

1. If you would like to know the time,
2. And when my sup - per - time is past

Just lis - ten and you'll hear,
And I must go to bed,

The bird in - side the cuck - oo clock
That bird in - side the cuck - oo clock

Is call - ing loud and clear:
Pops out his lit - tle head:

"Cuck - oo! Cuck - oo!
"Cuck - oo! Cuck - oo!

Cuck - oo! Cuck - oo! Cuck - oo!"
Cuck - oo! Cuck - oo! Cuck - oo!"

You will find the tonal pattern in the last two lines.
When you come to it, sing it with syllables.

sol sol mi mi

Teeter-Totter
ROTE–NOTE

Mary Thom

Eleanor Vaught

Smoothly

1. Tee - ter   tot - ter,   high and then   low,
2. Up and   down and   up and then   down,

Up-ward we   soar and then down-ward we   go;
Climb up   the moun - tain, look down on   the   town;

Bread and   wa - ter,   that is   our   song,
Bread and   wa - ter,   that is   our   song,

Come, Sal - ly Saw - ter, and   tee - ter a - long.
Bring Bil - ly Baw - ter, and   tee - ter a - long.

Sing the first and third phrases with syllables.

mi   do   mi

Mother's Song
ROTE – NOTE

Eleanor Vaught   Eleanor Vaught

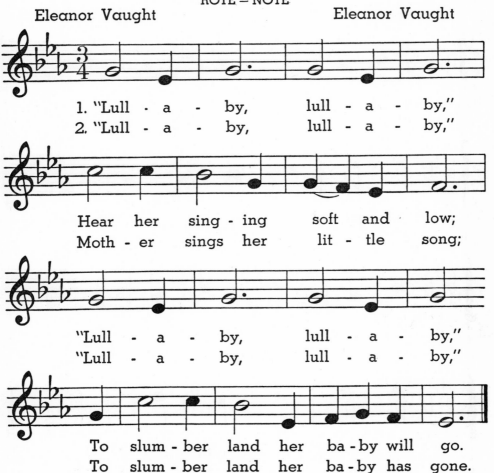

1. "Lull - a - by,   lull - a - by,"
2. "Lull - a - by,   lull - a - by,"

Hear her sing - ing   soft and low;
Moth - er sings her   lit - tle song;

"Lull - a - by,   lull - a - by,"
"Lull - a - by,   lull - a - by,"

To slum - ber land her ba - by will go.
To slum - ber land her ba - by has gone.

The new tonal pattern is lower than <u>sol-mi</u>.

The syllable name for the note on the first line of the staff is <u>do</u>.

(121)

sol mi do do

On the Seashore
ROTE — NOTE

Julie Gibault   Virgie Scott

1. On the   sea - shore   in   the   sum - mer,
2. Lit - tle   sun - beams   join   the   danc - ing,

When   the   sun   is   shin - ing   bright,
As   the   waves   go   splash - ing   by,

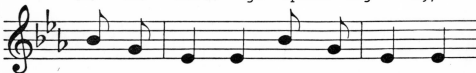

Then the   wa - ter   plays   and   danc - es
In   and   out   a - mong   the   sea   shells

In   the   blue   morn - ing   light.
They   are   play - ing   "I   Spy."

The two tonal patterns are joined together. Find
them. Sing them. Build them.

do mi sol

My Pony

ROTE–NOTE

Isabel Innes   Charles Crane

Jig - get - y jog - get - y o - ver the track,

Trot - ting a - long as we ride on your back;

Move a - long, po - ny, stead - i - ly go,

Jig - get - y jog, not too fast or too slow.

Find the tonal pattern in the song. Sing it. Sing the
rest of the song with "loo."

Pussy Willow

ROTE–NOTE

Isabel Innes   Jean Hoover

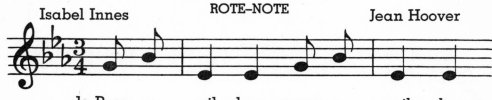

1. Puss - y wil - low, puss - y wil - low,
2. Now the tu - lip buds are wak - ing,

A - pril breez - es now be - gin to stir,
And they show their heads in sun - ny May,

Lit - tle birds could make a pil - low
Warm - er winds, your branch - es shak - ing,

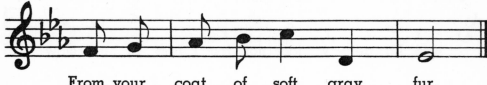

From your coat of soft gray fur.
Blow your fuzz - y coat a - way.

You know all the notes in the first and third phrases.
Sing them with syllables without help.

Waltz Song

ROTE

Clare Giffin

Czech Folk Tune

1. Who was it taught you to waltz in a ring?
2. Oh, it was Moth - er who taught me to waltz;

Who was it taught you to waltz in a ring?
Oh, it was Moth - er who taught me to waltz;

One, two, three, mer - ri-ly, One, two, three, mer - ri-ly,
One, two, three, mer - ri-ly, One, two, three, mer - ri-ly,

Who was it taught you to waltz in a ring?
Oh, it was Moth - er who taught me to waltz.

1. Stand on tiptoe and step <u>one</u>, two, three.
2. Come down on the whole foot on <u>one</u>. Make it a little louder than <u>two</u> and <u>three</u> (loud soft soft).
3. Join hands in a circle. Then move smoothly on this one-two-three or down-up-up pattern.

Barnyard Song
ROTE

Traditional

Folk Song
sung in Ohio

1. I had a roos-ter down by the barn gate,
2. I had a chick-en down by the barn gate,
3. I had a duck-ling down by the barn gate,

And that lit-tle roos-ter was my play-mate. *Sing Refrain 1.*
And that lit-tle chick-en was my play-mate. *Sing Refrain 2.*
And that lit-tle duck-ling was my play-mate. *Sing Refrain 3.*

Refrain 1.

My lit-tle roos-ter said: "Oo-dle dee-oo,

Go to Stanza 2.

Dee oo-dle dee oo-dle dee oo-dle dee oo."

Refrain 2.

My   lit - tle   chick - en   said: "Cluck   cluck   cluck,"

My   lit - tle   roos - ter   said: "Oo - dle   dee   oo,

Go to Stanza 3.

Dee   oo - dle   dee   oo - dle   dee   oo - dle   dee   oo."

Refrain 3.

My   lit - tle   duck - ling said: "Quack quack quack,"

My   lit - tle   chick - en   said: "Cluck   cluck   cluck,"

My   lit - tle   roos - ter   said: "Oo - dle   dee   oo,

End

Dee   oo - dle   dee   oo - dle   dee   oo - dle   de   oo."

Questions

ROTE

Christina G. Rossetti   J. Wolverton

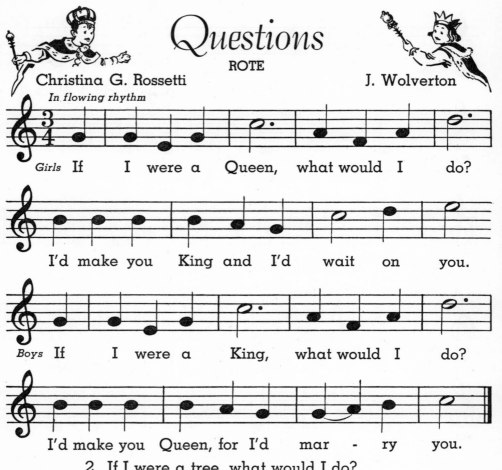

In flowing rhythm

Girls If   I   were a   Queen, what would I   do?

I'd make you   King and I'd   wait   on   you.

Boys If   I   were a   King, what would I   do?

I'd make you Queen, for I'd   mar - ry   you.

2. If I were a tree, what would I do?
   I'd spread my branches and wait for you.

   If I were a bird, what would I do?
   I'd build a nest, and I'd sing to you.

3. If I were a boat, what would I do?
   I'd spread my sails, and I'd wait for you.

   If I were the wind, what would I do?
   I'd puff and puff, and I'd wait for you.

Stanzas 2 and 3 were made by children in your grade.

(128)

sol sol do

Balloons
ROTE – NOTE

S. Spaeth   Beethoven

Swayingly

1. Float - ing high,   float - ing by,
2. See   them   go,   to   and   fro,

Red   and   pur - ple   and   yel - low;
Bright   and   clear   in   the   sun - light;

Each   bal · loon   will   be   soon
Through   the   air,   ev - 'ry - where,

Out   of   sight   in   the   sky.____
Far   as   breez - es   will   blow.____

The note in the fourth space of the staff is called <u>high</u>
<u>do</u>. Sing the first and third phrases with syllables.

(129)

do mi sol do

Firefly
ROTE–NOTE

John Bannister Tabb John Gardiner

Are you fly - ing through the night,

Look - ing where to find me?

No, I trav - el with a light

For the folks be - hind me.

You know all the notes of the tonal pattern.
Sing them. Then build them.

do   sol   mi   do

Frogs at Night
ROTE — NOTE

Ruth Jenkin   Ruth Jenkin

Frogs   that   sing   on   rain - y   nights

Make   such   an   aw - ful   noise,

They   should   all   be   sent   to   bed

Like   naught - y   girls   and   boys!

Sing all the syllables of the tonal pattern.
Find the tonal pattern in the song.

My Mother

ROTE

Irma Heath

J. W. Beattie

In flowing rhythm

1. Her face is sweet and kind— her way,
2. When bed-time comes as day-light ends,

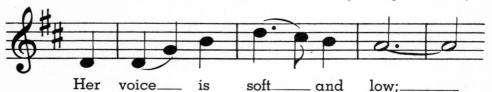

Her voice— is soft— and low;—
And eve-ning shad-ows creep,—

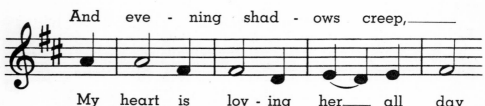

My heart is lov-ing her— all day
She helps me put my things— a-way

As 'round the house— I go.—
And sends me off— to sleep.—

Daddy and I

Adapted

ROTE

Mendelssohn

1. When sup-per is done in the eve-ning,
2. We sail on a ship or by air-plane
3. We see man-y peo-ple and plac-es

I stand by Dad-dy's chair,_____
To lands a-cross the sea,_____
From Lon-don on to Rome,_____

And when he has fin-ished his read-ing,
Where chil-dren are all ver-y friend-ly
But when we grow wea-ry of trav-el,

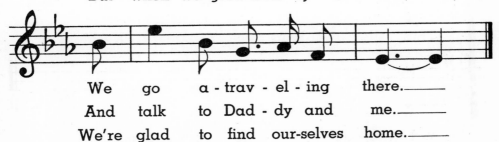

We go a-trav-el-ing there._____
And talk to Dad-dy and me._____
We're glad to find our-selves home._____

Robinson Crusoe

ROTE

Norma Gillett   Old Tune

1. Rob - in - son Cru - soe, a   sail - or was   he,
2. Dug   a fine home and then built him a   boat,
3. Lived man - y years in   his home by the   sea,
4. Rob - in - son Cru - soe, he wrote a fine   tale,

Fid - dle - dee - dee   fid - dle - dee - dee,
Fid - dle - dee - dee   fid - dle - dee - dee,
Fid - dle - dee - dee   fid - dle - dee - dee,
Fid - dle - dee - dee   fid - dle - dee - dee,

Lost   on   an   is - land far   out   in the   sea,
Tend - ed his   par - rot, his   dog, and his   goat,
One day came Fri - day,   a   fine ser - vant he,
Told all   a - bout his   re - mark - a - ble   sail,

Fid - dle - dee   fid - dle - dee - dee._____

Round the Mountain

ROTE

Traditional

American Folk Game

1. Here we go 'round the moun-tain, two by two,
2. Show us a live - ly mo - tion, two by two,
3. That is a live - ly mo - tion, two by two,

Here we go 'round the moun-tain, two by two,
Show us a live - ly mo - tion, two by two,
That is a live - ly mo - tion, two by two,

Here we go 'round the moun-tain, two by two,
Show us a live - ly mo - tion, two by two,
That is a live - ly mo - tion, two by two,

1–3. Rise up, sug - ar, rise._____

Make a single circle of partners.

1. Two partners stand in the center of the circle and plan
   what they will do. The others in the class sing and
   walk left around the circle.

2. While the class is still walking, the partners in the
   center make the motions that they have planned.

3. The others then make the same motions.

Three Dukes

ROTE

Traditional   Southern Singing Game

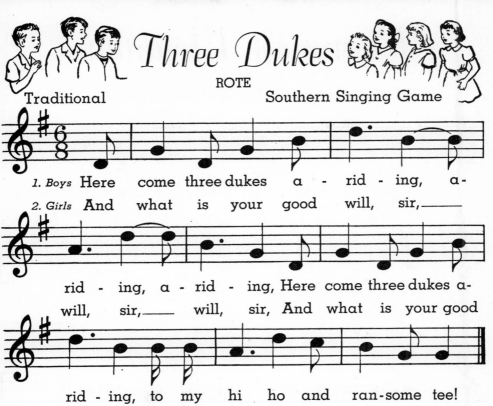

1. Boys Here come three dukes a - rid - ing, a-

2. Girls And what is your good will, sir,——

rid - ing, a - rid - ing, Here come three dukes a-

will, sir,—— will, sir, And what is your good

rid - ing, to my hi ho and ran-some tee!

will, sir, to my hi ho and ran-some tee!

3. Boys: Our will it is to marry, etc.

4. Girls: And which one will you have, sir, etc.

5. Boys: We think you look too dirty, etc.

6. Girls: We're just as good as you are, etc.

7. Boys: We'll take the prettiest maiden, etc.

The girls stand in a line. The boys stand in a line facing the girls.

On Stanzas 1, 3, and 5 the boys walk forward 8 steps and back 8 steps.

On Stanzas 2, 4, and 6 the girls do the same.

On Stanza 7 the head couple join hands and walk around the line of boys to the foot. Repeat the game.

All Around the Maypole

ROTE

Folk Song sung in Mississippi

All a-round the May-pole, May-pole, May-pole,

Begin to sing faster and clap

All a-round the May-pole, And now, Miss Sal-ly,

A little faster

Won't you dance for joy, Dance for joy, dance for joy,

Dance for joy, And now, Miss Sal-ly, won't you dance for joy?

And now, Miss Sal - ly, won't you bow?

Join hands and form a circle around a child standing in the center. The child is "Miss Sally."

All walk around singing until you begin to clap for Miss Sally, who dances. When Miss Sally bows, she bows in front of a child, who then takes her place.

Miss Sally may jump for joy, skip for joy, or make any other motions she pleases.

Thread the Needle

ROTE

Traditional   American Singing Game

The thread fol - lows the nee - dle,

The thread fol - lows the nee - dle,

To and fro the nee - dle will go,

Mak - ing the stitch - es all in a row.

Stand in a line and join hands.

One child stands at the head of the line. He is the "needle." He weaves in and out between the joined hands until he comes to the foot of the line.

Repeat the game, with the new "needle."

Go Away, Partner

ROTE   German Singing Game

Adapted

O   go a - way, go a - way, part - ner,

Stand in place, and motion with your hands.

O   come to me, come to me, part - ner,

Step to the right to face a new partner.

Cling,   clang,   hei - di,

Clap your hands.   *Clap partner's right hand.*   *Clap your hands.*   *Clap partner's left hand.*

Both   your hands   you   give   to   me,

Partners join both hands and turn each other around.

Tra la la la la, tra la la la la la la la.

Make a double circle, with partners facing each other.
Then sing and play the game as often as you like.

do ti la sol fa mi re do

The Chimes

ROTE — NOTE

Mina Dawson   Mina Dawson

The chimes ring out a pret - ty tune,

They tell the time of day;

"Do ti la sol fa mi re do"

Their mu - sic seems to say.

The tonal pattern is called the <u>scale</u>.
Sing the syllables for the first and third phrases.

(142)

do re mi fa sol la ti do

Turtle and Rabbit

NOTE

Isabel Innes

Nancy Rogers

Slowly

Tur - tle, tur - tle, you old slow poke,

Don't you ev - er try to run ver - y fast?

In a race you'd be a big joke,

Sure - ly you would al - ways be the last.

What kind of notes are there in this song?
Read the words in rhythm.
You know all the syllables of this song.
Sing the song with syllables. Then sing it with words.

Tonal Patterns

How many of these tonal patterns can you sing?

Choose a pattern that you know. Sing it. Ask some-
one to tell you the number of the pattern that you sang.

If he tells you correctly, it is his turn to sing.

Make some melodies using some of the tonal patterns.

(144)

My Swing

ROTE

Evelyn Corey   J. Wolverton

1. My swing, O my swing on the ap-ple bough,
2. My swing, O my swing on the ap-ple bough,

Car-ry me high   to   the blos-soms   now;
Car-ry me low   thro' the grass-es   now;

slower

Car-ry me high   as the flight of   a   bee,
Car-ry me low   as the brook run-ning free,

in time

My swing, O my swing in the   ap-ple tree.
My swing, O my swing in the   ap-ple tree.

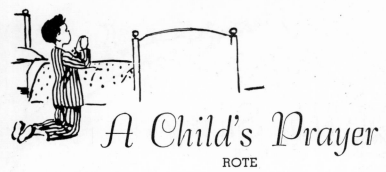

A Child's Prayer

ROTE

German Folk Song sung in Wisconsin

1. Soft   the shad - ows round me   creep,
2. Keep,   O Lord, my friends so   dear,

Soon   I'll   close my eyes in   sleep,
All   whose love pro - tects me   here,

Fa - ther of us all, I   pray,——
Bless all peo - ple great and small,——

Guard my bed till break of   day.
Look in kind - ness on us   all.

April

ROTE

Adapted

German Folk Song

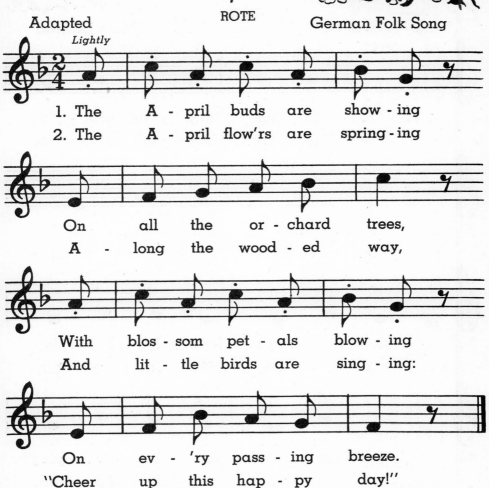

Lightly

1. The A - pril buds are show - ing
2. The A - pril flow'rs are spring - ing

On all the or - chard trees,
A - long the wood - ed way,

With blos - som pet - als blow - ing
And lit - tle birds are sing - ing:

On ev - 'ry pass - ing breeze.
"Cheer up this hap - py day!"

A dot under or over a note means: "Sing the note short."

(147)

The Rain
ROTE

Nancy Rogers   Mina Dawson

Lightly

1. Lis - ten   to   the   drip - ping, drop - ping
2. Lis - ten   to   the   drip - ping, drop - ping

Of   the   rain   On   the   pane!
Of   the   rain   On   the   pane!

Lit - tle   rain - drops,   light - ly   hop - ping,
Com - ing   all   the   day   in   show - ers,

slower

Do   you   think   they'll   soon   be   stop - ping?
Help - ing   thirst - y   gar - den   flow - ers.

In time

Lis - ten   to   the   drip - ping, drop - ping
Lis - ten   to   the   drip - ping, drop - ping

Of the rain On the pane!

Of the rain On the pane!

The Robin's Return

ROTE

Evanston children   Evanston children

Happily

Last fall a rob - in flew a - way,

I thought that he___ had gone to stay,

But one day not___ so long a - go,

That ver - y same rob - in sang: "Cheer - i - o!"

Easter Greeting

ROTE

Adapted   German Folk Song

1. Hap - py   chil - dren,   lift your   voic - es,
2. As the   wak - ing   earth re - joic - es,

Join the   cho - rus,   ris - ing   gay;
And the   flow'rs their   mes - sage   bring,

Win - ter's   o - ver, spring has   found us,
Chil - dren,   join your   hap - py   voic - es

And it's   East - er   to -   day.
In a   greet - ing   to   spring.

Gifts of God

ROTE

Adapted

J. S. Bach

1. Who has giv'n the sun its bright - ness,
2. Who has taught the birds their mu - sic,

Light - ed stars in— eve - ning skies?
Made the for - est— breeze re - joice?

All day long and while we're sleep - ing
When the breeze and birds are sing - ing,

God is smil - ing— through their eyes.
What we hear is— God's own voice.

Moving Day

One day Mr. Do said to his wife: "Mrs. Do, I would like to move to a new house."

"I am tired of this house too," said Mrs. Do.

Mr. Do said: "I found a house not far away. It is in the first space."

So they moved.

Mr. Mi met Mr. Do on the street.

"Mr. Do," he said, "where have you moved? I saw a 'For Rent' sign on your old home."

Mr. Do said: "I moved not far away. I live in the first space."

"I would like to move too," said Mr. Mi. "Do you know where I could live near you?"

"Oh, yes," said Mr. Do. "There is a house up the street. It is not far away."

"Thank you," said Mr. Mi.

He was in such a hurry that he ran all the way home.

"Mrs. Mi," he said, "let us move."

"I would like to move to a new house," said Mrs. Mi.

So they moved.

What do you think Mr. Sol did? Yes, he moved too.

do   mi   sol

Moving Day
ROTE — NOTE

J. Wolverton   J. Wolverton

Do and Mi and Sol have moved,

Each to homes not far a - way;

First space, sec - ond space, third space too.

Here they live in their hous - es new.

In what phrases do you find the tonal pattern?
Build it.   Play it on your instruments.

Animal Talk

ROTE–NOTE

Adapted

English Folk Tune

1. Joe and his   dog were out - side for a   walk,
2. "Why," said the   dog," when you   hear my bow - wow,
3. Tree toad and crick - et and   ka - ty - did,   too,

Try - ing to   learn how small   an - i - mals   talk.
I am just   talk - ing the   best I know   how."
Each has his   own spec - ial   lan-guage for   you.

Play and sing the tonal pattern in the first phrase.
Sing the rest of the song with words or "loo."

do *mi* *sol*   *do* *re* *mi*

The Merry-go-round

NOTE

J. W. Beattie   Old Tune

1. Far down the street I can hear a gay sound,
2. Po - nies and ze - bras and el - e-phants too,

Mer - ry - go - round!   Mer - ry - go - round!
Mer - ry - go - round!   Mer - ry - go - round!

Or-gan and an - i - mals whirl-ing a - round
An - i - mals just like the ones in the zoo

Rid - ing the mer - ry - go - round._____
Ride on the mer - ry - go - round._____

You have one old and one new tonal pattern.
Find both of them in the song.

Mister Bear

ROTE — NOTE

Vivian Kronenberg   Vivian Kronenberg

Child 1. "Mis - ter Bear, what do you eat?"
2. "Mis - ter Bear, when do you sleep?"

Bear "Grubs and ber - ries ver - y sweet."
"When the win - ter snows are deep."

Child "Mis - ter Bear, when do you play?"
"Do you sleep the win - ter through?"

Bear "In the sum - mer ev - 'ry day."
"Yes, my lit - tle friend, I do."

Sing the first and third phrases with syllables.
Play them on your instruments.

Schoolroom Helpers

ROTE

J. Wolverton

J. Wolverton

All 1. Each one of us must do his share
1st Child 2. I wa - ter all the lit - tle plants
2d Child 3. When Moth - er comes to vis - it us,

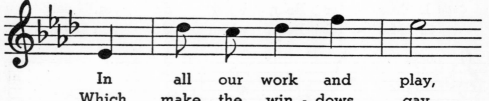

In all our work and play,
Which make the win - dows gay,
I help her find a chair;

To make our school-room clean and bright
They can - not grow un - less I give
We show her all the work we do

Through ev - 'ry hap - py day.
A drink to them each day.
And books we like to share.

Chant the rhythm.

Indian Mother's Song

ROTE — NOTE

Mayme Christenson   Alma Spear

1. Gen - tly sing - ing winds
2. Soft - ly wood - land sounds

Ba - by's cra - dle swing - ing,
Through the trees come creep - ing,

While my fire I tend,
Sun - shine all a - round,

Lull - a - bies I'm sing - ing.
War - rior child is sleep - ing.

Learn "Indian Mother's Song" in a new way.

You sing all the re's, and the teacher will sing the rest of the song.

Do the same with mi and do.

When you know the song, sing all the syllables.

Rhythm and Melody Game

CLOUDS

White sheep, white sheep,
On a blue hill,
When the wind stops,
You all stand still;
When the wind blows,
You walk away slow;
White sheep, white sheep,
Where do you go?

Christina G. Rossetti

1. Chant the poem.
2. Make your own melody for the poem.

The Oriole

ROTE

J. W. Beattie   J. Wolverton

Swayingly

1. O - ri - ole,   o - ri - ole,
2. O - ri - ole,   o - ri - ole,

Nest - ing so high I scarce - ly see;
Car - ry - ing food for ba - bies three;

Sweet your song, All day long,
Here and there, Ev - 'ry - where,

Swing - ing in yon - der tree._____
Sing - ing a song____ for me._____

Try some good high and low swings to this music.
Sway as the tree or the nest sways with the wind.

Spring Song

ROTE

Cecil Cowdrey　　　　　　　　　　　　John Davey

Not too slowly

1. High, high in the old ap-ple tree,
2. Sweet, sweet from the old ap-ple tree,

I hear a moth-er bird sing-ing for me;
Blos-soms in show-ers drift down up-on me;

Cheep! cheep! un-der-neath her warm breast,
Soft, soft sings the rob-in, cheep, cheep,

There are her ba-bies so snug in the nest.
Put-ting her three lit-tle rob-ins to sleep.

Form small groups to make "nests."
Each group then sways to the rhythm of the song.

(163)

Bouncing Ball

ROTE

Audrey Carpenter   J. Wolverton

1. I know a jol - ly game to play
2. If I can bounce it twen - ty times,

With my new rub - ber ball,____
When I grow up I'll be____

I bounce it up and down the street
A cir - cus clown that rides a pig

Or up a - gainst a wall;____
As round and fat as he;____

If   I   can bounce it   fif - teen times
And when   I bounce it   twen - ty - five

With nev - er once   a   slip, ____
I   think I'm ver - y   smart, ____

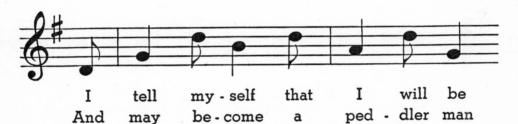

I   tell   my - self that   I   will be
And may be - come   a   ped - dler man

A   sail - or   on   a   ship. ____
Who drives a horse and cart. ____

After you have learned to bounce the ball to the music, try some new ways:

1. Bounce the ball as you walk forward.
2. Bounce it as you move in a circle.
3. Bounce it to a partner.

The Little Birds' Ball

ROTE

Folk Song
sung in Indiana

1. The spring bird— said   to   the   night - in - gale:
2. The wood-peck-er came from his   hole   in the tree
3. The   wren   and the cuck - oo— danced with de-light;
4. They sang   and— danced till the sun   was— low,

"I___ mean   to   give   the___   birds   a   ball;
And— brought his   bill   to   the   com - pan - y;
The—   rav - en walked with the yel-low bird's wife;
Then the moth - er   birds   pre -   pared   to   go;

___   Bird - ies   great   and___   bird - ies   small,
___   Ber - ries   ripe   and___   ber - ries   red,
The   awk - ward   owl   and the   bash - ful   jay
___   Bird - ies   great   and___   bird - ies   small,

All — must come to the lit-tle birds' ball."
"A ver-y long bill," the — lit-tle birds said.
— Bid — each oth-er a ——— ver-y good day.
— All — flew home from the lit-tle birds' ball.

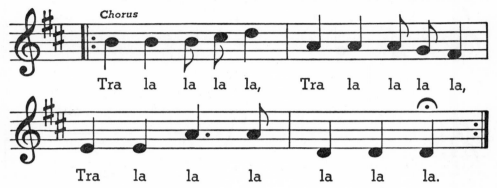

Chorus

Tra la la la la, Tra la la la la,

Tra la la la la la la.

Choose a partner and dance at "The Little Birds' Ball."

re sol mi sol

Rocking Chair
ROTE-NOTE

Mayme Christenson   Alma Spear

1. Grand - ma   in   her   rock - ing   chair,
2.   I   sit   in   the   rock - ing   chair,

Rock - ing,   rock - ing,
Rock - ing,   rock - ing,

Knit - ting   things   for   me   to   wear,
  I   make   songs   and   sing   them   there,

Rock - ing,   rock - ing.
Rock - ing,   rock - ing.

Chant the rhythm.
Sing the song with syllables.   Sing it with words.

sol fa mi

Night Time

ROTE – NOTE

Ann Donaldson   Eleanor Vaught

Soft   the   breez - es   blow,

Wa - ters   mur - mur   low,

Hoot   owl's   lone - ly   call,

Dark - ness   cov - ers   all.

Find the tonal pattern in the song.

The teacher will sing the first two notes of each phrase. You sing the tonal pattern.

After you know the melody well, sing the song with syllables and then with words.

sol   mi   fa   re

The Cuckoo
ROTE–NOTE

Adapted   German Folk Song

1. Cuck-oo! Cuck-oo! Wel-come your song;
2. Cuck-oo! Cuck-oo! What is your song?
3. Cuck-oo! Cuck-oo! Tell us of spring;

Win-ter is go-ing, Soft winds are blow-ing;
I hear you sing-ing, I see you swing-ing;
Sun-beams are play-ing, Tree-tops are sway-ing;

Spring-time, spring-time Soon will be here.
An-swer, an-swer, Why do you call?
Wak-en, wak-en! That is your call.

How many fa's do you find?
How many re's do you find?

sol   la   sol   mi

The Squirrel

NOTE

Isabel Innes   Nancy Rogers

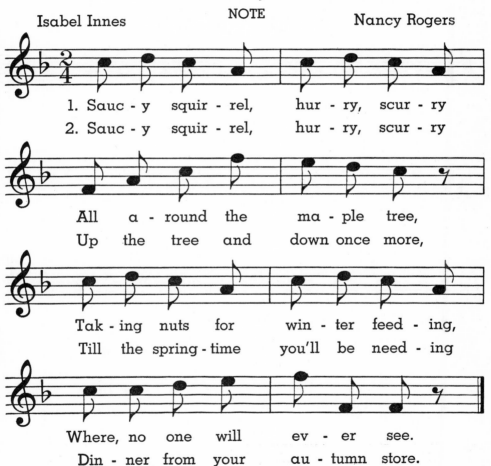

1. Sauc - y   squir - rel,   hur - ry,   scur - ry
2. Sauc - y   squir - rel,   hur - ry,   scur - ry

All   a - round   the   ma - ple   tree,
Up   the   tree   and   down once   more,

Tak - ing   nuts   for   win - ter   feed - ing,
Till   the spring - time   you'll   be   need - ing

Where, no   one   will   ev - er   see.
Din - ner   from   your   au - tumn   store.

La is the name of the note on the fourth line of the staff.
Sing and build the tonal pattern.

(171)

The Windmill

NOTE

Translated

French Folk Song

la   la

Look a-cross the green and grass-y hill,

You can see the far-mer's bus-y mill;

How the wind with whist-ling sound

Moves the long arms round and round!

My Whistle

ROTE

Dorothy Aldis

Harold P. Wheeler

Gaily

I want to learn to whis-tle,

I've   al - ways   want - ed   to;____

I   fix   my   mouth   to   do   it,

But   the   whis - tle   won't   come   through.____

I   think   per - haps   it's   stuck,   and   so

I   try   it   once   a -   gain.____

Can   peo - ple   swal - low   whis - tles?____

Where   is   my   whis - tle   then?____

The Birds' Chorus

ROTE

Virginia Murdock   Old Tune

1. Out   in   the   wood-lands   a   glad cho-rus sings,
2. See   them go   dart - ing   from   bush   or   from   tree,

Keep - ing   in   time   to   the   flut - ter   of   wings;
Feath - ers   the   bright - est   you   ev - er   did   see;

Rob - in   and   flick - er   and   o - ri - ole   gay,
Cat - bird   and   spar - row   and   car - di - nal   red,

Thrash - er   and   war - bler   and   nois - y   blue jay.
Wood - peck - er   tap - ping   the   time   with   his   head.

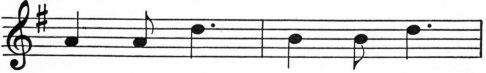

"Sweet - sweet - sweet!   Tweet - tweet - tweet!"
Rap - rap - rap!   Tap - tap - tap!

All of them join in the sing - ing.
Mes - sage of sum - mer they're bring - ing.

Tonal Patterns

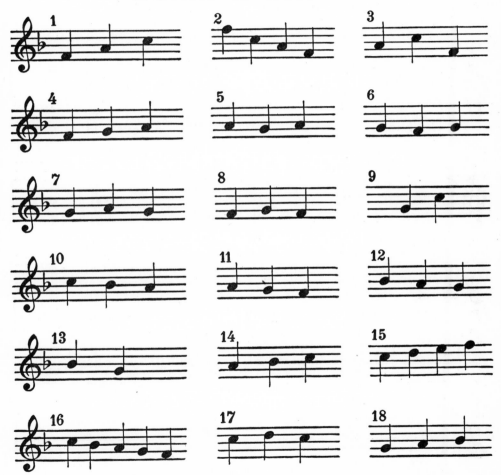

How many tonal patterns can you sing? How many can you build?

A Trick on Mr. Rabbit

Adapted from a folk story   Harold P. Wheeler

THE WATER IS GONE

Sadly and slowly

The animals of the forest sing:

The wa-ter is gone, and the for-est is dry;

We must have wa-ter or we all will die;

The creek is dry and the riv-er, too;

Now what must thirst-y an-i-mals do?

slower

What must thirst-y an-i-mals do?

DIGGING THE WELL

Animals: We'll all get to-geth-er with shov-el and spade

And dig and dig till a well is made.___

We're dig-ging and dig-ging a hole in the ground,

Deep - er and deep - er till wa - ter is found.

Animals: Here is the water!   How good it tastes!

Mr. Fox: Mr. Rabbit, why didn't you help us?

Mr. Rabbit: I don't like to work.

Animals: Then you can't have any of the water.

Mr. Rabbit: You'll see!   *(He hops away.)*

WHAT SHALL WE DO?

Animals: What shall we do to guard our well
And keep it safe to-night?

Mr. Bear: I'll be the guard who will growl and growl
And give Mis-ter Rab-bit a fright.

The animals leave. Mr. Bear stands beside the well. He hears a song far away.

COO–RI–LOO–RI

Slowly

Mr. Rabbit: Coo - ri - loo - ri, coo - ri - loo,

Here is sweet hon - ey that's just for you.

Coo - ri - loo - ri, coo - ri - lay,

You will find it by danc - ing a - way.

Mr. Bear listens and then starts to dance.
He dances off to find the honey.

Mr. Rabbit hops in and drinks all of the water in the well.
He hops off into the forest when he hears the animals coming.

Animals (yawning and stretching): Where is Mr. Bear?

Mr. Giraffe: I can't see him anywhere.

Mr. Elephant: I can't feel any water with my long trunk.

All Animals (wailing): Oh, the water is gone!

Mr. Wolf: I see Mr. Rabbit's tracks all around the well.

WHAT SHALL WE DO?

Animals: What shall we do to guard our well

And keep it safe to - night?

Mr. Monkey: I'll be the guard who will chat-ter and chat-ter

And give Mis - ter Rab - bit a fright.

The animals leave. Mr. Monkey stands beside the well. He hears a song far away.

COO–RI–LOO–RI

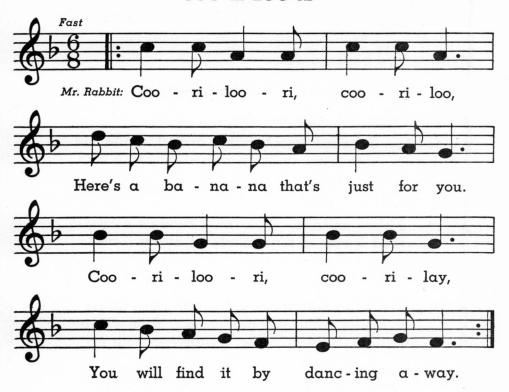

Fast

Mr. Rabbit: Coo - ri - loo - ri,   coo - ri - loo,

Here's a ba - na - na that's   just   for   you.

Coo - ri - loo - ri,   coo - ri - lay,

You will find it by   danc - ing a - way.

Mr. Monkey dances. Then he goes to find the banana. Mr. Rabbit hops in and drinks up all the water. He hops away when he hears the animals coming. He hides.

Animals: Where is Mr. Monkey?

Mr. Elephant: Here are Mr. Rabbit's tracks around the well.

Animals: We have no water!

They all cry.   Mr. Monkey comes in.

Animals: Why did you leave the well?

Mr. Monkey: I heard sweet music and it made me dance away.   Mr. Rabbit played a trick on me!

Animals: We will catch him.

Mr. Fox: I have an idea.   In Farmer Brown's corn field I saw a man made of straw.   He scares away the crows.

Mr. Wolf: That won't scare Mr. Rabbit away.

Mr. Monkey: I know what to do!   You make a straw man, and I will get inside.   Then when Mr. Rabbit comes, I will reach out my long arms and catch him.

Animals: That's a good idea.   We will catch him and tie him up.   Then he can't get away!

A STRAW MAN

Animals: We'll all get to-geth-er, for we know a way

To catch him when he comes a - long to - day;

We're mak-ing a straw man with Mon-key in-side,

We'll catch Mis-ter Rab-bit be - fore he can hide!

The animals hide near the well to watch for Mr. Rabbit.

COO–RI–LOO–RI

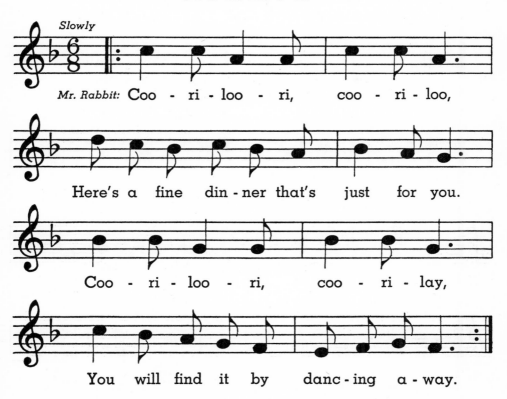

Slowly

Mr. Rabbit: Coo - ri - loo - ri, coo - ri - loo,

Here's a fine din - ner that's just for you.

Coo - ri - loo - ri, coo - ri - lay,

You will find it by danc - ing a - way.

Mr. Rabbit comes nearer and nearer to the Straw Man, as he sings his song.   He is very angry.

Mr. Rabbit: Why don't you dance, Straw Man?

He sings again the first phrase of his song.

Mr. Rabbit: Get out of my way, or I will hit you!

He hits the Straw Man with his right paw.
Mr. Monkey reaches out and grabs it.

Mr. Rabbit: Let go, let go, or I will hit you again!

He hits the Straw Man with his left paw.
Mr. Monkey grabs it.   Mr. Rabbit howls and
tries to get away.   The other animals come in
and tie up Mr. Rabbit.   They form a circle
around him and sing:

LOOK AT MR. RABBIT!

Animals: Look at Mis-ter Rab-bit, fas-tened tight!

You'll not rob our well to - night.

We will go a - bout our way

While you must stay here,— tied, all day.

The animals dance and sing.

COO–RI–LOO–RI

Animals: Coo - ri - loo - ri, coo - ri - loo,

There is no wa - ter or food for you.

Coo - ri - loo - ri, coo - ri - lay,

We are go - ing and you— must stay.

America

Samuel Francis Smith   Henry Carey

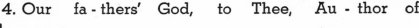

1. My coun-try, 'tis of thee, Sweet land of
2. My na-tive coun-try, thee, Land of the
3. Let mu-sic swell the breeze, And ring from
4. Our fa-thers' God, to Thee, Au-thor of

lib-er-ty, Of thee I sing; Land where my
no-ble free, Thy name I love; I love thy
all the trees Sweet free-dom's song; Let mor-tal
lib-er-ty, To Thee we sing; Long may our

fa-thers died! Land of the Pil-grims' pride,
rocks and rills, Thy woods and tem-pled hills,
tongues a-wake, Let all that breathe par-take,
land be bright With free-dom's ho-ly light;

From ev-'ry moun-tain side, Let free-dom ring!
My heart with rap-ture thrills Like that a-bove.
Let rocks their si-lence break, The sound pro-long!
Pro-tect us by Thy might, Great God, our King.

Classified Index

(187)

Rhythm Patterns in Rote, Rote-Note, and Note Songs

$\frac{2}{4}$ Run, run, run, run:
16, 20, 29, 41, 49, 61, 64, 74, 100, 101, 107, 108, 111, 112, 143, 147, 148, 168, 171, 172

$\frac{4}{4}$ Run, run, run, run:
15, 37, 51, 88

$\frac{4}{4}$ Walk, walk, walk, walk:
35, 54, 60, 72, 73, 93, 106, 113, 118, 130, 131, 142, 151, 154

$\frac{2}{4}$ Run, run, walk:
97, 103, 148

$\frac{2}{4}$ Walk, run, run:
34, 90, 104

$\frac{2}{4}$ $\frac{3}{4}$ Slow, slow:
67, 68

$\frac{3}{4}$ Walk, walk, walk, slow:
46, 48, 57, 62, 90, 92, 116, 125, 128, 134, 155, 156, 170

$\frac{4}{4}$ Slow, walk:
14, 138, 169

$\frac{3}{4}$ Slow, walk:
28, 38, 47, 52, 99, 120, 121, 132, 149, 162

$\frac{3}{4}$ Run, run, walk, walk:
122, 124, 150

Intervals and Sequences in Rote, Rote-Note, and Note Songs

sol-mi
11, 28, 32, 52, 60, 61, 74, 78, 85, 97, 108, 109, 116, 118, 120, 147, 169, 170

mi-sol
27, 34, 52, 61, 97, 103, 111, 147

sol-mi-do
10, 12, 13, 32, 66, 73, 90, 104, 114, 122, 126, 132, 137

do-mi-sol
18, 21, 22, 24, 30, 36, 38, 70, 74, 81, 123, 124, 131, 134, 137, 154, 155, 156

sol-fa-mi-re-do
9, 21, 30, 35, 45, 48, 66, 90, 92, 104, 111, 112, 124

do-re-mi-fa-sol
11, 31, 72, 74, 168, 172

sol-la-ti-do
20, 36, 51, 61, 171

do-ti-la-sol
11, 18, 36, 45, 48, 66, 90, 92, 113, 122, 130, 148, 171

do-sol
9, 106, 107

do-sol
20, 43, 57, 67, 72, 106, 169

sol-do
15, 26, 37, 51, 53, 62, 80, 85, 112, 129

sol-do
11, 29, 50, 68, 104, 106, 107, 121

do-mi
29, 51

mi-do
28, 51, 62, 121, 138

do-mi-sol-do
45, 46, 52, 123, 130, 171

do-sol-mi-do
45, 60, 129, 131

fa-re
13, 29, 32, 34, 41, 46, 51, 57, 60, 66, 71, 73, 74, 78, 88, 103, 116, 118, 132, 145, 147, 169, 170

re-fa
14, 26, 27, 66, 78, 88, 103, 111, 112, 134

re-ti
24, 26, 27, 60

ti-re
20, 85

Index of Songs